Practical CUMF

CONSERVATION
WATER AND WETLANDS

Hodder & Stoughton

LONDON SYDNEY AUCKLAND

Practical

CONSERVATION

Open University Course Team

Andrew Lane (Course Team Chair)

Susan Carr (Lecturer)

Pamela Furniss (Project Officer)

Graham Turner (BBC Producer)

Jennie Moffat (Course Co-ordinator)

Julie Bennett (Editor)

Lesley Passey (Designer)

Keith Howard (Graphic Artist)

Roy Lawrance (Graphic Artist)

Sue Snelling (Secretary)

ISBN 0 340 53368 4

First published 1992
Copyright © The Open University 1992

Designed by the Graphic Design Group of The Open University

Typeset by The Open University

Printed in the United Kingdom for the educational division of Hodder and Stoughton Ltd, Mill Road, Dunton Green, Sevenoaks, Kent by Butler & Tanner Ltd, Frome and London

Contents

This book is produced by The Open University as part of the *Practical Conservation* training programme which deals with all aspects of conservation on land that is managed largely for commercial or recreational purposes (see Figure 0.1).

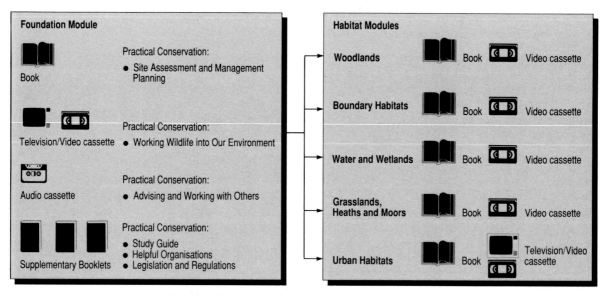

Figure 0.1   The Open University teaching programme for Practical Conservation

The foundation module covers site assessment and land use management planning in general and includes:

▶ a foundation book;

▶ a video cassette of a 50 minute television programme;

▶ a 60 minute audio cassette;

▶ two supplementary booklets;

▶ a *Study Guide* to the full programme.

This book with its accompanying 30 minute video cassette forms one of a series of modules on practical aspects of conservation management for a range of habitats:

▶ Woodlands;

▶ Boundary Habitats;

▶ Water and Wetlands;

▶ Grasslands, Heaths and Moors;

▶ Urban Habitats.

These training materials are suitable for use by groups or by individuals, studying alone or in association with a formal course. For those who would like to gain practical experience or a qualification, the Open University training programme is being incorporated into courses offered by colleges, field centres and other training bodies.

For further information please write to: Learning Materials Service Office, The Open University, PO Box 188, Walton Hall, Milton Keynes MK7 6DH.

Chapter 1

INTRODUCTION

Rivers and streams, ponds and lakes, marshes and bogs, canals and reservoirs – these are some of the most noticeable of all features in the countryside. Our attention is drawn both to the presence of water in the landscape and to the sights and sounds of the enormous variety of plants and animals that live in, on or near it. Wet habitats are immensely valuable to wildlife and the continuing existence of a great many species depends on the maintenance of wet areas. However, in many cases these are threatened habitats, which have been, and continue to be, destroyed, because their commercial value is seen to be insignificant. There has been considerable pressure over many years to make these areas more productive for people, which has led to a marked reduction in the extent and quality of wet habitats. Fens and marshland have been drained to allow ploughing, for improved pasture or for urban development. Rivers have been straightened and dredged to improve drainage, for flood control and for navigation. Urban, industrial and agricultural wastes have all contributed to the pollution of watercourses. Ponds have been lost through neglect and deliberate infilling.

With the loss of habitat there is an associated reduction in the distribution and numbers of many species of plants and animals that depend on wet areas. For example, there used to be 41 species of dragonfly in Britain, but since 1953 four species have become extinct, three of these due to pollution and the lowering of water tables. Redressing the balance a little are new areas of open water created as reservoirs and in flooded former gravel pits.

Wet habitats are dynamic ecosystems, and even if left completely untouched by humans, many would change into other, often less valued, wildlife habitats by natural processes, such as silt accumulation in ponds or the growth of scrub in ditches. On the other hand, some are so fragile that the best management is to protect them from any interference at all.

To avoid further losses of wet habitats, to enhance existing ones and to create new water bodies and wetlands all requires careful management, and the first step is to draw up a management plan.

1.1   Management planning

Most water and wetland areas have been managed or influenced by human activities and, in the past, this has often been for one particular purpose. It is now realised that protection and enhancement of the environment must be incorporated into any use of water and its surrounding land. A management plan provides a mechanism for integrating the conservation of wildlife and landscape with other land uses. Management planning is essential for all forms of land use, but especially for resolving the conflict between commercial and non-commercial factors.

Management planning in general is dealt with in the foundation book, *Practical Conservation: Site Assessment and Management Planning.* Stage 1 integrates landscape and wildlife conservation assessment with a consideration of the business, recreational or other aspects of land use; Stage 2 identifies the land manager's objectives and the relevant constraints; Stage 3 involves exploring and choosing the options for achieving the objectives identified; Stage 4 involves drafting a formal plan of action; and Stage 5 is putting the plan into practice and monitoring progress.

Existing management levels

It is quite likely that any area of water or wetland that you know is already managed in some way, but the type of management and the degree of control will vary widely. The National Rivers Authority is responsible for the management of the main rivers of England and Wales. Its functions include the licensing and monitoring of abstractions and impoundments, environmental quality and pollution control, land drainage and flood protection, fisheries, conservation and recreation and, in some areas, navigation. In Scotland, these responsibilities are shared by the River Purification Boards and the local authorities. At the other end of the management scale, some small ponds or boggy field corners are the responsibility of individual landowners and may have been ignored and untouched for years.

Some sites have been recognised as extremely rare or endangered and so take on an additional importance. Many of these have been given special status, which provides a certain level of statutory protection and control. Environmentally Sensitive Areas (ESAs), Sites of Special Scientific Interest (SSSIs), National Parks and Areas of Outstanding Natural Beauty (AONBs) in England and Wales, and National Scenic Areas (NSAs) in Scotland are all subject to special regulations and laws, which land managers must follow. There is a special status specifically for wetlands that are important waterfowl habitats. These are known as Ramsar sites, because they were designated in accordance with the provisions of the convention on Wetlands of International Importance signed at Ramsar, Iran in 1971. There are 40 Ramsar sites in the United Kingdom.

If you are responsible for an area designated as having special status, you will know how this affects your activities, and you should discuss your plans with the Nature Conservancy Council, the Countryside Commission or whatever regulatory body is appropriate to your circumstances.

Manager's attitudes

A very important aspect of management planning is to recognise the importance of the manager's preferences. Any plan that goes against the manager's natural inclinations will not be given the long-term commitment needed to put it into practice. If you are an adviser or consultant, understanding the prejudices, interests, likes and dislikes of your client(s) will be an important part of your job. Even if you are a land manager yourself, and more or less in control of the situation, you may need to give this some careful thought, for example before deciding how to react to advice that you are given or how to respond to new opportunities to create wet habitats.

Usually, you should develop a general management plan for any area of land before going on to consider the place of water and wetlands within it. This becomes particularly important if you are thinking of creating new water habitats, for example a pond. Under these circumstances, you first need to answer the question: 'Is a pond an appropriate use of this site?' If the site is already valuable, for example as herb-rich grassland, making a pond would result in a net conservation loss. You also need to consider how the long-term management of the pond can be fitted in with any other commercial objectives. For any new development, you should only proceed if the general management plan indicates that, *all things considered*, it is the best use of the land.

This book and the associated video cassette concentrate on three particular aspects of management planning: assessment (Stage 1), management options

(Stage 3) and implementation (Stage 5). If you are preparing a management plan, or if you already have one, these materials will help you to put it into practice. Even if you do not want to become involved in management planning, they will help you to assess the present conservation value of wet habitats, to decide what can be done to maintain or improve them, to choose good sites and species mixtures for the creation of new water bodies and wetlands, and to implement these ideas.

Whether your site is of international importance or a boggy corner in a field, the same principles of management planning should apply. The important thing is to understand what you are doing and why, and to bear in mind the following simple guidelines.

Positive guidelines

▷ Think before you act.
▷ First assess your area for its conservation and commercial value.
▷ Consider as many options as possible.
▷ Draw up a management plan, however brief.
▷ Monitor changes in the area, good and bad.
▷ Be prepared to change your plans.

1.2   *How to use this book*

Several of the chapters contain exercises for you to do, which are printed on a green background. The exercises are based on what you have read, and should be carried out on an area to which you have legitimate access. In addition, there are two case studies, one dealing with ponds and wetland areas on a farm and the other with river management, which will give you a wide range of examples to illustrate the activities described in the book and show how they can be done. The case study sections at the end of the chapters collectively give a complete picture of planning for practical conservation. The case studies have each been prepared by individuals who have direct personal knowledge of the site in question.

The 30 minute video cassette that complements this book illustrates practical conservation measures in all types of water and wetlands. Throughout the book the video cassette symbol in the margin indicates topics that are illustrated on the video cassette. (Please note that on the video cassette, for brevity the word 'wetlands' is used to mean all types of watercourse, water body and wetland.)

A list of books that can provide further reading is given in Appendix I. Many of the terms and concepts used when discussing water and wetlands have different meanings to the public and the scientist, or the same feature may be described in different ways. It is important to understand these distinctions in order to follow any advice that you are given. In this book, the most important and widely used terms and concepts are highlighted in bold type the first time that they appear in the text and are explained in the Glossary (Appendix II). Throughout the text, plants and animals are referred to by their common names, but to assist in precise identification, a list of the scientific names of the plants is given in Appendix III.

In this book there are several references to the foundation book, *Practical Conservation: Site Assessment and Management Planning,* and you will find it helpful to have access to a copy.

General information on sources of advice and grants is given in the two supplementary booklets in the foundation module, *Helpful Organisations* and *Legislation and Regulations*, and will not be repeated here. Both this book and the video cassette refer to the practical skills needed and safety aspects to be considered when working with water, but there is no substitute for experience, and you should, if necessary, attend a training course that will show you how to handle tools and machines correctly. Such courses should be available locally through the Agricultural Training Board, the British Trust for Conservation Volunteers or some agricultural colleges.

1.3   Categories of water and wetlands

This book covers all freshwater habitats, but not coastal or brackish waters. Freshwater habitats are defined as habitats that have some permanent water throughout the year. They divide roughly into open water habitats of river, stream, pond and lake on the one hand, and wetland habitats, such as marsh, bog, fen and swamp, on the other.

Many sites will have a mixture of different habitats, which grade from one type to the next. For example, the source of upland streams is often indistinct, as small rivulets emerge out of a bog making it impossible to define precisely the start of the watercourse; the gradually sloping edge of a lake may show a succession of vegetation types from open water through swamp or marsh to dry land, but the boundaries of each zone will not necessarily be easy to see.

It is often difficult to categorise a particular site, and strict pigeon-holing is probably best avoided. However, some distinctions must be made, and Table 1.1 defines the major types of wetland and open water habitats.

Table 1.1 Major types of water and wetlands

Open water	
River/stream	Natural watercourse with permanently running water
Canal	Artificial channel, usually originally for transport
Wet ditch	Small, artificial channel containing water, usually for drainage
Pond	Small area of still water, may be natural or artificial
Lake and reservoir	Larger area of still water; lakes may be natural or artificial, reservoirs always the latter
Wetlands	
Marsh	Water-logged mineral soil in which water level seldom rises above surface at any time of year
Swamp	Mineral-based soil normally flooded throughout the year; usually dominated by tall, emergent plant
Bog	Permanently wet peat resulting from high water table and/or high rainfall in acid conditions; vegetation dominated by bog mosses
Fen	Permanently wet peat that lacks extreme acidity due to presence of alkaline groundwater; also used to describe a vegetation type
Carr	Wet woodlands, usually of willow and alder

Although many watercourses, water bodies and wetlands are of natural origin, relatively few have remained untouched by people over the centuries. Rivers and streams are mostly natural, but have frequently been straightened, deepened or otherwise interfered with, and may have lost all semblance of naturalness. Many of the lakes in upland areas of Britain were formed as a result of glaciation.

Most of the ponds in England and Wales are artificial, probably originally constructed as watering places for livestock. They may have developed largely by accident, due to trampling, or have been deliberately constructed by farmers who tapped springs, built small dams and made water-tight bases with **puddled clay**. Larger ponds, lakes and moats would have been constructed for manor houses and monasteries. These would provide water for livestock, for keeping fish, for fire-fighting and, possibly, for storage of drinking water.

Abandoned quarries have a tendency to flood and create new lakes. Some worked-out gravel pits are now deliberately managed as wildlife sanctuaries, particularly for water birds. The Norfolk Broads were formed as a result of digging peat for fuel. Originally they were dry pits, from which peat was excavated until the fourteenth century, but then the water level rose and they were eventually abandoned and became the interconnected systems of lakes and rivers that we see today.

Marshes, bogs and fens are natural features created by particular combinations of climate, geology and landform. They used to be far more extensive than they are today; much of the East of England was once fenland. Drainage of these wetlands dates back to Roman times and has continued ever since at an increasing rate, particularly in the last few decades. All that are left now are the last few isolated remnants of the former wetland landscapes.

Ditches, including **drains** and **dykes**, have been dug since pre-Roman times. Their functions were to drain the land, to act as boundaries, for flood control, irrigation and even navigation. During the seventeenth century, the Somerset Levels were drained for agricultural purposes, creating the system of pastures divided by **rhynes**, which now provide a rich environment for wildlife. In fact, the rhynes are relict features and demonstrate the type of habitat that formerly covered the entire area. It is ironic that this important wetland habitat, recently threatened by modern agricultural improvement, was, in fact, created in the course of agricultural improvement.

The way that a watercourse, water body or wetland originated and developed will determine its basic features. These will be influenced by human activities, and by a combination of the physical, chemical and biological processes taking place in and around the water. Rivers and streams may change their course as the moving waters erode the banks and deposit the sediment downstream. Sediments and organic matter accumulate in the still waters of ponds and lakes, so that open waters are gradually converted to wetland and then finally to dry land, as part of an aquatic **succession** (as illustrated in Figure 3.6(b) of the foundation book). Successions of vegetation will also occur in peat bogs and other wetland areas, and will, in time, proceed to the final stage of woodland, unless prevented by the prevailing conditions, such as the water level, the absence of particular nutrients or the presence of grazing animals.

The growth of vegetation is another important factor in the structure and development of wet habitats, with different types of vegetation found in different zones of the wetland habitat. Dying vegetation adds to the organic matter present, while living plants can help to trap silt or stabilise banks. The many zones that can occur in wet areas are a major reason for their diversity and richness, but they are also subject to rapid change as a result of drought, flood and human disturbance. It is therefore important to recognise both the dynamics and the fragility of these valued habitats.

1.4   The case studies

The following descriptions form the background to the two case studies.

Borders Farm

Location

The first case study area is situated in the Scottish Border Hills (Southern Uplands). It is a 445 hectare farm, on the south side of the meandering River Ettrick. The land rises from the river bank at 220 metres to an altitude of 466 metres. Rainfall ranges from 1100 to 1500 millimetres per annum.

Geology

The rock is principally Upper Silurian flags, grits, greywackes and shales, giving a high, rounded relief with some broad, glaciated valleys and more recent, deeply incised, smaller valleys. A patchwork of **fluvio-glacial** sands and gravels, boulder clays and more recent **alluvial** deposits overlies parts of the area.

Soils

Soils are all of the Ettrick series, comprising a mix of brown forests, non-calcareous gleys, peaty podzols and peat, plus occasional, more recent, riverine alluvium-derived soils. The improved ground supports acid bent–fescue grassland, oak and birch woodland, heath–rush–fescue grassland and, on higher ground, **blanket bog** and flying-bent bog.

Land capability

The land is mainly class 4, 5 and 6. This is due to soil limitations throughout, plus wetness and gradient limitations in some areas. There are a few areas of riverside class 4 land, which could accommodate a forage crop rotation. [In Scotland, the Land Capability Classification for Agriculture is on a scale from 1 (best) to 7 (poorest).]

Land use

The farm shows little obvious evidence of early settlements, with no significant archaeological features. For a long time the land use has been restricted to hill grazing with a little **inby land** in the valley bottom.

In the 1920s the Forestry Commission began planting parts of the Border Hills with conifers. A post-war surge of planting spread through the region, with a further peak in the 1960s and 1970s. This planting has included parts of the Ettrick Valley area, and the farm has some extensive conifer blocks on its south-west side, plus some smaller blocks on the better land, which provide good stock shelter and an improved shoot.

When the current landowner arrived in early 1986, he set about diversifying the landscape and habitats through a series of measures, most notably:

▶ planting mixed blocks of woodland with shelter, game and wildlife in mind;

▶ creating a wide range of water and wetland habitats;

▷ clearing some areas in the larger conifer blocks to provide good, open-space habitats and deer lawns.

The use of the 445 hectares currently stands as follows:

Permanent pasture*	42 hectares
Hill grazing	235 hectares
Commercial forest	146 hectares
Other woodland	16 hectares
Pond and wetland features	6 hectares

(*Sixty per cent of the permanent pasture yields silage; stubble turnips may also be grown in rotation.)

The land is in a Less Favoured Area (see the *Legislation and Regulations* booklet in the foundation module). The stock kept comprises 500 ewes and 40 suckler cows, and other land uses include a private shoot, fishing (private and let) and two holiday cottages.

The 6 hectares of water and wetland features are composed of a wide range of ponds, **flashes**, **mires** and **flushes**. These are seen as an asset, to be protected, enhanced and, where possible, replicated elsewhere on the farm, while at the same time being carefully integrated into other land uses.

Some sites are designated primarily for fishing, others for duck-flighting and some purely for wildlife. Good design and careful conservation have ensured that all the water and wetland features have a definite wildlife benefit. There is no conflict of interests between agriculture and conservation, as generally it is only a little rough grazing that is lost from the agricultural side. Stock are denied access to the ponds, as their water needs are adequately provided for by burns and springs on the hill. The springs are periodically excavated into small pools to which animals have access, using a JCB-type excavator that is permanently on the farm.

In terms of advice, a private forestry consultant is used for silviculture, while the Nature Conservancy Council and Borders Farming Forestry and Wildlife Advisory Group have both given advice on other aspects of conservation on the farm.

The River Ouse, Buckingham

The second case study covers approximately 4 kilometres of the valley of the River Ouse south-east of Buckingham. The river here is typically some 5–10 metres wide, 0.5–1.5 metres deep and has a **bankfull capacity** of approximately 12 cubic metres of water per second.

Location

The upper 0.5 kilometre of the river around Bourton Mill flows through approximately 16 hectares of low-lying flood plain, bounded on the eastern (downstream) edge by a new ring-road bridge. New residential areas surround it on both sides, but the **flood plain** itself was designated as an amenity grassland in 1979 planning reports and has escaped any development. Part of the flood plain is currently leased to farmers for cattle grazing. The majority of the land in this area is owned by the Buckingham Borough Development Company (BBDC).

Site 1

The main river flows eastwards along the southern edge of its immediate flood plain, while a backwater ditch also dissects the area along much of the northern edge, collecting surface storm water draining off the residential areas on that side. The main river used to flow through Bourton Mill, to be joined by the backwater downstream of the mill site. However, the mill is in disrepair, as is the mill weir, and the main river now escapes over a side weir just upstream of the collapsed mill weir. The side weir is, in fact, the mill's derelict sluice-way and the river now flows north-eastwards along the line of the original mill bypass channel to join the backwater ditch. Together they rejoin the original main river channel downstream of the mill.

Site 2

Downstream of the ring-road bridge, the valley widens out and the river meanders between farmland on both banks, predominantly semi-improved pasture. A partly eroded weir at Maids Moreton adds variety to the flow pattern by retaining a section of deep, slow-flowing water immediately upstream. Fringes of vegetation occur along much of the river, although the banks are generally fairly steep. They may be up to 2 metres in places, but have water-level shelves where slumping has occurred. Trees are largely absent, except for a few mature willows. Although it is a routinely managed watercourse, the river channel has retained a varied structure of **pools**, gravel **riffles** and **shoals**.

Flooding

The river valley experiences flooding problems typical of many watercourses that drain urban areas. The building of new housing estates on either side has led to a great increase in storm water run-off into the river. Maximum storm water discharges from these new developments, when coinciding with high levels in the river (expected on average once a year), cause flooding, both of the agricultural land downstream of the town and of certain urban areas within Buckingham.

Responsibility for flood protection and land drainage lies with the Anglian Region of the National Rivers Authority (previously the Anglian Water Authority), although it does not own the rivers or their banks. In addressing the problems in the Buckingham area, the Authority's aims were as follows.

1   To balance and control storm water discharges into the river in order to prevent an increased incidence of flooding of agricultural land downstream.

2   To improve the efficiency of the surface water sewers draining from the new residential areas in order to prevent urban flooding.

3   To minimise the environmental impact of the scheme and to further conservation.

At the same time, proposals were put forward by the BBDC and Aylesbury Vale District Council (AVDC) to open up the river corridor for amenity and recreation. A further aim, therefore, was to ensure that the opportunity was taken to begin creation of a linear park in the 0.5 kilometre stretch of land upstream of the ring-road.

Integration of engineering and environmental interests was seen as a key component early on in the process of design and construction of the river works. Biological surveys, extensive consultation with interested bodies, close supervision of works and close liaison between the project engineers and the conservation officer were all seen as key features of the scheme.

Chapter 2

ASSESSING WATER AND WETLANDS
IN THE LANDSCAPE

Water often occupies a special place in the landscape. The sinuous course of a bubbling river flanked by trees, the shimmering expanse of a lake reflecting the clouds, both catch the eye and provide a contrast with the straight-edged, brown or green fields that frequently surround them.

The attractiveness of water is not just due to its scenic presence, but also to its high recreational value. People are drawn to the sights, smells and sounds of water, which can evoke memories of happy childhood days paddling and picnicking, and inspire them to write poetry and paint pictures, or make them feel peaceful and contented.

There is a fundamental relationship between the landscape and flowing water, as it is the rivers and streams that help to shape the land into valleys, hills and slopes. The development of river valleys takes place over millions of years, but the effects of moving water can be much more immediate. As water flows over land, fragments of rock and soil are picked up by the water and then deposited further downstream. The processes of erosion and deposition are influenced by several factors, including the hardness of the rocks, the stability of the soil and the velocity and volume of the moving water. Rivers will cut deeply into sands and gravels and will frequently erode away their banks, especially on the outside of meanders. When the speed of flow decreases, as it does on the inside of a meander, the particles suspended in the water will be deposited.

The power of water to shape the landscape is not entirely restricted to flowing water in streams and rivers. The effects of wind on still waters can create significant waves, particularly on large lakes, and wave action at the water's edge will cause erosion of the banks. Much of the specific shape and character of the margins of large lakes is determined by the varying effects of wind on different shoreline materials, and on the orientation of storm winds to the shore. If the shore is rock, waves may break up the weaker types of rock and leave harder material projecting as ridges. If the shore is soft sand or peat, waves quickly erode the edge, perhaps into distinct cliffs. If the edge is gravel or similar material, waves carry away finer particles but leave larger stones and boulders in place. The disturbed materials will be deposited on the lake bottom, grading from coarse particles near the shore to fine particles in deeper water.

Any increase in wave action may destroy the stability of the shoreline. On canals, rivers and lakes that carry powered boats there are frequently problems of bank erosion caused by the wash that the boats create. The faster the boats travel, the greater the size of the wash wave and the greater the potential damage to the bank.

In rivers, the erosive powers of the water increase with its velocity and volume. For any particular watercourse, the volume of water that it carries at any one time will reflect the quantity of recent rainfall in the **catchment area**. The shape of the watercourse will be determined not by the average water flow but by the peak flows, which may only occur a few times each year. Highland streams and rivers, for instance, are subject to sudden and

13

severe spates after heavy rain, which will not only erode the banks but will often wash away most of the vegetation, even that growing at some considerable height above the normal water level. The river bed material may also reflect extreme rather than average conditions. For example, a stream strewn with large boulders is clearly moulded by torrential spates rather than by average flow or volume.

Watercourses, water bodies and wetlands are often the major focus of a landscape, and other features are assessed in relation to them. Thus, when these areas are full of rubbish, or have been excessively altered by engineering work, this detracts from the whole landscape, not just the water itself. It is therefore important for all existing and any new areas of water to be sensitively managed. The starting-point for any new developments should be a landscape assessment.

2.1   General landscape assessment

Landscape assessment in general involves obtaining an overall impression of the land and how the details fit together to make up the whole picture. This will depend on the variation, from one area to another, in:

▷   the landform (the underlying 'skeleton' of rocks and soil);

▷   the covering of vegetation;

▷   the buildings and historical and archaeological features (structures);

▷   the cultural associations of the area concerned;

▷   the human needs that the area fulfils.

At this general assessment stage, you should consider the water and wetland areas in the context of the landscape as a whole, particularly their importance and appropriateness to the scenery.

The assessment should also reflect people's attitudes and social influences. Landscape is a valuable public resource and should be assessed and planned with this in mind.

General landscape assessment was described in Chapter 2 of the foundation book. It involves:

▷   selecting several viewpoints to give a complete coverage of the area in which you are interested;

▷   marking these on a map of the area and filling in a checklist for each viewpoint;

I DONT THINK YOU'RE MEANT TO TAKE PHOTO'S FROM IN THE RIVER....

▷   recording your impressions formally, using notes, photographs, sketches and maps (not forgetting to consider your personal preferences and perceptions and the needs and desires of other people who may have an interest in the area).

It is important to keep systematic records and, if appropriate, to divide up the holding into clearly recognisable zones to provide a basis for the long-term management of the land.

For a more detailed assessment of the areas of existing water and wetland, you need to focus your attention particularly on:

- physical features of the water/wetland area(s);
- vegetation in and around the area(s);
- the presence of any features of archaeological interest;
- public views of the area(s).

Physical features of the water/wetland

It is important first to define the area in which you are interested. You may be looking at a small area, such as a village pond or a stream, in which case the area of study is probably quite easily defined. You should include a few metres of land around the water, as this can be very important for many plants and animals and should be considered as a part of the wet habitat. Alternatively, you may be surveying a whole farm, in which case you may well have several discrete wet habitat areas. Whether to group them together or deal with them separately will depend on their type, proximity and similarity. There may be circumstances common to several different areas, such as a common source of water or similar vegetation, that may justify considering all wet areas together, but they will probably also benefit from individual attention if time allows.

In some cases, it may be difficult to decide where the boundary of a particular wetland lies. There will be a gradual change from, for example, a marshy area to the surrounding better-drained meadow. If, for the purposes of sketching the area, you have to decide on a particular boundary line, remember that this is really a fuzzy line and so any future activities should not necessarily be bounded exactly by this limit.

Size and shape

The impact of water and wetland areas on the landscape is strongly influenced by their size and shape. Large features will dominate the scene, whereas small streams and ponds may hardly be visible at all. For open water bodies, the shape of the water, whether it has curved or angular edges, may influence your view of its appropriateness in the landscape. Some landscapes, such as rolling hills, have many curves, and angular features would look out of place. In other landscapes, the character is derived from small-scale features, and a large body of water would be out of scale and inappropriate.

Size is not easy to measure, as boundaries are seldom straight, but it may be possible to pace out the maximum dimensions in two or three directions or, for an approximately circular feature, to pace around the circumference.

Origins and history

The origins of a water body or wetland may also be important: whether it is natural or artificial and, if the latter, when it was created and for what purpose.

Very few water and wetland areas are untouched by human activity, with only some upland streams, bogs and lakes likely to be truly natural. The features associated with the natural appearance of a river would be a winding course with an irregular river bed and bank slope, patches of various water weeds and a variety of bankside vegetation. A heavily managed river, on the other hand, would be straight, with a regular bank slope and no vegetation in or next to the water. Straightening of rivers and the removal of vegetation was thought, in the past, to be essential to achieve the river engineer's aims of flood control and improved drainage. Fortunately, in the last decade or so, a more enlightened approach has been taken by river

15

engineers, and devastating river works are now rarely seen, although many watercourses still suffer from the ruinous practices of the past.

Using shape and pattern to work out the origins and past history of water and wetlands requires some caution. Appearances can be deceptive and, as in the Norfolk Broads, what appears to be natural may in fact be artificial. However, the value of the features may be undiminished by this. The rhynes of Somerset and similar wet ditches on Otmoor in Oxfordshire and other old grazing marshes are artificial channels, built as 'wet fences' and drainage channels between meadows. They follow a pattern of straight lines – a totally unnatural feature – yet because of their long history and consequent rich flora and fauna, they have an extremely high value as a habitat for wildlife, as well as being an essential component of a peaceful landscape.

More accurate and detailed historical information about an area may be obtainable from your library, local record offices or local historical societies.

Vegetation

The basic features of the landscape as described above are covered and moulded by the presence of trees, shrubs and other plants. When looking at the vegetation as a landscape feature, it is the visual impact and overall influence on the appearance of the site that matters, so identification of species is not required at this stage. Obviously, the visual dominance of the vegetation will vary considerably with the seasons, and you should bear this in mind when doing an assessment.

Of particular importance is the presence of large shrubs and trees: whether they screen off a wetland, whether they hang over the water margin, whether they shade water from the sun. It is not only important to site these correctly when creating new wetlands or water bodies, but it is also import-ant not to remove them unnecessarily, for example to gain access to a site for engineering works.

In terms of visual impact in the landscape, most other plants will not be significant, although there are some exceptions, such as a clump of tussock sedge, a stand of reeds or other tall, emergent water plants.

Archaeological features

Many wetlands, for example the Somerset Levels, the East Anglian Fens and some bogs of western and northern Britain, contain some of the most important archaeological remains in the country. The water-logged ground conditions mean that softer materials, such as wood, leather, rope and even human bodies, are preserved for thousands of years, as well as stone, metal and pottery items, which are more usually found. Since most of these remains lie buried and do not show on the surface, they are prone to accidental damage. This may be through drying after lowering of the water table or removal of vegetation, or physical damage resulting from ditch cleaning or peat cutting.

In contrast to the great age and invisibility of archaeological remains buried in wetlands, there are many water features that are themselves of great historical interest. A prime example is the increasingly rare dew ponds of farmland. Dew ponds occur mainly on chalk downland, and are mostly circular in shape and fairly shallow. They were built using an ingenious method of construction, which provided for a large catchment area to collect water and at the same time kept evaporation to a minimum. A number of dew ponds remain today, but many have fallen into neglect because they have become redundant with the development of piped field water supplies.

Conserving ancient features need not be at odds with current land practices. Indeed, grants may be available for their maintenance. Advice and help on these matters are available from your local county archaeological officer and the appropriate national bodies listed in the *Helpful Organisations* booklet in the foundation module.

The public view

Usually water features are a pleasure in any landscape, but there can be exceptions. If the water is heavily polluted with oil or farm waste, its appearance and odour may inspire disgust rather than delight. Ponds and streams seem to attract rubbish and litter, which are unpleasant in any environment.

The speed of flow of watercourses can influence the impression that they make, according to the sound produced. Babbling brooks, roaring torrents and gently gliding streams will all provoke different feelings.

The line or pattern created by water may also be a noticeable feature of a landscape: for example, the sinuous course of a meandering river as it winds along a valley or a collection of small ponds creating a dotted pattern when viewed at a distance.

The person who owns or manages a piece of land inevitably sees it differently from outsiders. Any landscape assessment should take account of both points of view, that of the manager of the land or the person who has the power to take decisions about it, and those of members of the public who may drive past it, walk near it or view it from a distance.

In particularly important landscape areas, where a public interest has been formally declared by their designation as National Parks, AONBs or NSAs, the landowner or manager of the area always needs to be aware of any special restrictions on the management of the land (see the *Legislation and Regulations* booklet in the foundation module).

2.2   Making your own wetland landscape assessment

In the previous section, the elements of landscape assessment were described, but the only way to learn more about this is to do it yourself.

As suggested in Chapter 1, choose an area of water or wetland to which you have legitimate access and make a landscape assessment of it. Remember that, ideally, you should first assess the place of the water or wetland in the landscape as a whole, as described in the foundation book and summarised briefly here, before going on to assess the water or wetland itself. At this stage, you should use maps to mark viewpoints and significant features, and photographs, sketches and checklists to record the present state of the landscape, both as a basis for planning changes and as a reference point against which to measure the effects of any changes.

General landscape assessment

1 Gather background information on the geology of the area and the history of the locality, including any archaeological records.

2 Draw a sketch map of the area (or use an Ordnance Survey map) and mark prominent features within, and outside, it. Annotate the map with comments on these features and mark any distinct landscape zones.

3 Make sketches or take photographs showing views that include the water/wetland area(s). Mark each viewpoint on your map. Include any viewpoints that are important to the general public, for example views of the water from main roads, as well as those of personal interest to the landowner or manager.

4 Fill in a checklist of landscape assessment features for each viewpoint (using the case study example in Table 2.2 on p. 22 for guidance). Make notes describing:

▷ the reason for choosing each viewpoint, particularly noting anything of public interest;

▷ the size, shape and pattern of the water/wetland area(s);

▷ the scale of the water/wetland area(s).

5 Describe your personal perceptions of the landscape for each viewpoint (using Table 2.1 on p. 21 for guidance).

Water and wetland landscape assessment

1 Make close-up sketches or take photographs of the watercourse, water body or wetland area, taking care to include any notable features, such as islands or steep banks. Identify any areas with particularly interesting characteristics, such as old, **pollarded** willows. Draw a sketch map of the water/wetland area(s) and mark on it the close-up viewpoints chosen.

2 Add notes or annotate the sketches or photographs and maps, describing:

▷ the drainage pattern if known, i.e. the source and outlet of the water;

▷ trees, shrubs and other significant vegetation, both in and around the water;

▷ historical and archaeological features;

▷ your personal perceptions.

3 Record any special designations or uses of the water/wetland area(s), e.g. National Parks, AONBs, NSAs, SSSIs, ESAs; public access, footpaths, bridleways; ancient monuments.

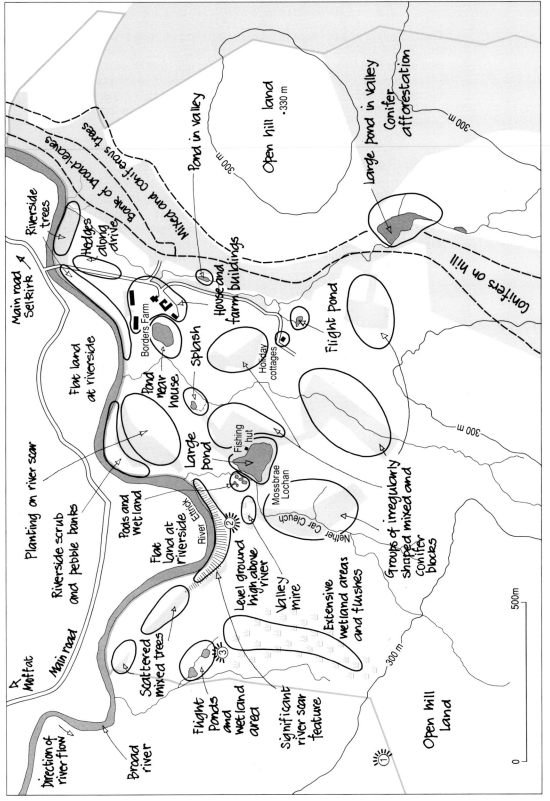

Figure 2.1   General landscape features of Borders Farm

19

2.3 Landscape assessment of case study areas

The following examples of landscape assessment, based on the two case studies described at the end of Chapter 1, will give you some guidance, but remember that they are personal views. Do not treat them as rigid templates; as you become more experienced you will develop your own variations on the method and level of detail required. Note also that it has not been possible to include all the figures and tables produced in the actual case studies.

Borders Farm

The farm sits on a series of old river terraces on the southern shore of the River Ettrick. This gives a ranked effect to the landscape from all viewpoints, with a good concept of the depth of the view. This is all superimposed on a broad, glaciated valley with rounded hills and many small burns running into the river. A patchwork of conifer and mixed plantations breaks up the landscape further. The general landscape features of the farm and the location of three selected viewpoints are shown in Figure 2.1.

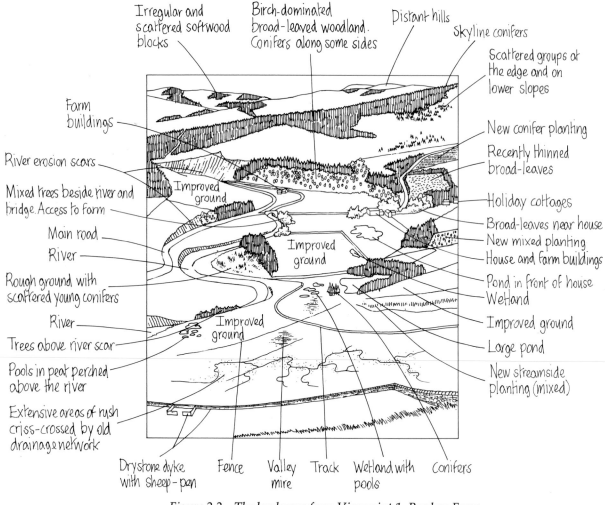

Figure 2.2   The landscape from Viewpoint 1, Borders Farm

From this high point there is a long-distance view, taking in the tallest distant hills, the patchwork of conifer plantation and the complex mix of landforms and habitats immediately around the farm buildings and inby land. Figure 2.2 is a sketch view of the landscape from this viewpoint. A green sweep of good land follows the riverside, with land rising away to the left and right.

The landscape is marked by heavily incised river scars, some of which are broken up by broad-leaved and mixed woodlands. Looking down, following the line of the drystone dyke, the land slopes away to the left towards the river and is criss-crossed with a network of drains. Patches of wet ground with small pools are picked out by the sunlight.

A wealth of aquatic habitats is visible: the river, ponds, **splashes**, mires and streams. Many of the edges are quite hard and straight. Drystone dykes form many of the boundaries and are far more bold and noticeable than fence lines. To the left, the main road meanders east, following the curves of the river.

A landscape perception of the area is shown in Table 2.1 and the landscape features from Viewpoint 1 are summarised in Table 2.2 (overleaf).

Table 2.1 Landscape perception from Viewpoint 1, Borders Farm

Criterion	Suggested descriptions*
Scale	Intimate, small, large, vast
Enclosure	Tight, enclosed, open, exposed
Variety/diversity	Uniform, simple, varied, complex, surprising
Harmony	Well balanced, harmonious, discordant, chaotic
Movement	Dead, calm, lively, busy, frantic
Texture	Smooth, rough, coarse-grained
Naturalness	Wild, unmanaged, remote, undisturbed
Tidiness	Untidy, neat, over-managed
Colour	Monochrome, subtle, muted, colourful, garish
Smell	Pleasant, unpleasant, obnoxious
Sound	Intrusive, noisy, quiet
Rarity	Ordinary, unusual, rare, unique, familiar
Security	Comfortable, safe, intimate, unsettling, threatening
Stimulus	Boring, monotonous, bland, interesting, surprising, invigorating
Beauty	Ugly, uninspiring, pretty, attractive, majestic, picturesque

(Source: Adapted from Countryside Commission, 1987)

*The lists in this column are not intended to imply a scale of values from good to bad; the words are not arranged in any particular order.

Table 2.2 Checklist of landscape features: landform, vegetation and structures for Viewpoint 1, Borders Farm
Grade the relative contribution of each feature as follows: *inconspicuous; **noticeable; ***conspicuous.

Land holding	BORDERS FARM	Viewpoint number 1

Date 8/3/91

Time of day 9.30 am

Weather Clear and bright

Landform

Plain	Coast	Marsh ✳✳✳	Lake ✳✳✳
Lowland	Estuary	Mudflat	Pond ✳✳✳
Plateau	Broad valley ✳✳✳	Dune	River ✳✳✳
Hill ✳✳✳	Narrow valley ✳	Beach	Stream ✳✳
Crag or cliff ✳✳	Deep gorge ✳		Canal
Mountain			Ditch ✳✳✳

Slopes

Vertical ✳	Steep ✳✳	Gently sloping ✳✳
Undulating ✳✳	Flat	

Vegetation

Woodland

Broad-leaved woodland ✳✳	Mixed woodland ✳✳✳
Coniferous woodland ✳✳✳	Scrub ✳✳

Heathland and grassland

Heather moorland ✳✳✳	Bracken ✳
Upland grass moor ✳✳✳	Lowland heath
Peat bog ✳✳✳	Lowland unimproved grassland
Water meadow	

Cultivated land

Arable land	Market gardens and orchards
Improved pasture ✳✳✳	Parkland

Linear features

Hedgerows	Roadside verges
Woodland fringe ✳✳	Railway embankments
River banks ✳✳✳	

Small isolated features

Isolated trees ✳✳	Small shelter-belts ✳✳
Groups of trees, mainly broad-leaved (less than 0.25 ha) ✳✳✳	Copses and spinneys ✳✳
Groups of trees, mainly coniferous (less than 0.25 ha) ✳✳	Small gardens ✳

Structures

Buildings ✳✳✳	Fences ✳✳
Farmyards ✳✳	Walls ✳✳✳
Camp sites	Telephone wires
Car parks	Electricity pylons
Quarries ✳	Rubbish dumps
Industrial land	Derelict land

Occasional walkers come through the farm, using the track that is prominent
in the foreground of the view shown in Figure 2.3 to reach the open hill.
There is a natural-looking but created wetland with pools below the large
pond (lochan). The dam is well screened behind a small block of conifers,
which was left intentionally when the remaining area was cleared to give
space for the large pond.

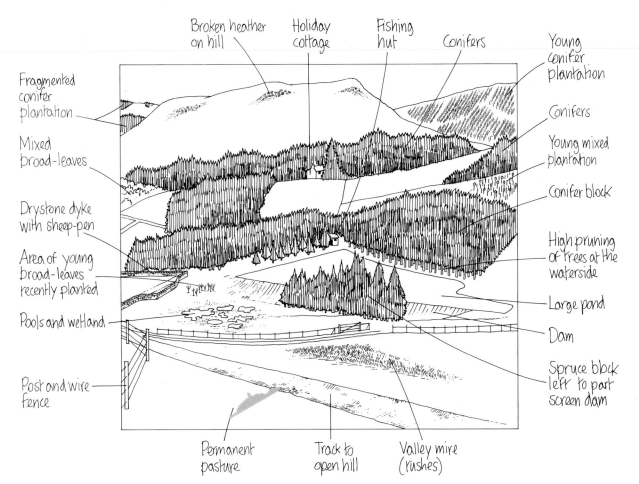

Figure 2.3   The landscape from Viewpoint 2, Borders Farm

A fishing hut is half concealed behind the trees selected and left standing at
the water's edge when the land was cleared. This looks intriguing because it
is not completely visible. Behind the large pond, ranks of odd-shaped conifer
and mixed plantations give the landscape perspective.

Further away, the hill land rises more steeply. A young conifer plantation is
stark and obvious in the background to the right – straight lines are very
evident. There is an old, stone-built holiday cottage nestling just over the hill
with groups of mixed trees half concealing it.

The large pond was created in something of a hollow at the break of slope
onto an earlier river terrace, now deeply cut into by the river turning the
bend. A considerable number of conifers were cleared to accommodate the

pond, although some were left standing below the line of the dam. These two aspects of the site of the pond combine to ensure that it is well concealed, not attracting undue attention, yet an evident feature once one is on the farm.

This view looks away from the farm itself, west along the valley, and out over two flight ponds. The image contrasts with the other viewpoints and shows another aspect of the area's landscape.

Here, the landscape is more simple and open, with the rolling contours of the foreground and middleground defined by drystone dykes, and a backdrop of high hills. A bold, dark strip of spruce and larch (the latter adding some variety) is a stark feature, and conceals the contours of a marked valley that cuts deeply into the hillside. The hilltops are high, but rounded and undulating. Much of the hill is 'white', comprising grasses and rushes. Heather is patchy, dark and very noticeable where it occurs.

A river meander is just visible, picked out by alder, willow and ash, which grow along the bank. Around the flight ponds, trees have recently been planted and, in time, should provide attractive, sheltered water: a feature that should draw duck down.

The River Ouse, Buckingham

Lying at the upper end of the Ouse catchment, the river valley sides are not steep, but the flood plain is a marked feature, although it is not particularly wide. The river itself is often hidden or indistinct, due in part to the lack of fringing bankside trees, such as willows, to accentuate its course. Similarly, there are no wetland marshes or **flood meadows** adjacent to the river, rather an almost monotonous range of semi-improved pastures.

The area of study divides into two distinct landscape zones, with the new ring-road bridge acting as the dividing line (Figure 2.4). Upstream, the 0.5 kilometre of river corridor is part of the encroaching urban fringe, whereas downstream there are almost uninterrupted agricultural views.

This is an area of open pasture land in what has recently become an urban development area. Although it has no landscape designations, it is recognised as an area of amenity grassland ready for inclusion within a linear, riverside park. The viewpoint selected for more detailed analysis is on the riverbank just upstream (north) of the footbridge closest to the old mill weir.

The residential areas to the north-east and south of the site are built on raised ground and are therefore visible from most locations along the river at this point. The general lack of trees in the foreground results in unbroken views of the housing estates across a flat, rather featureless, rough pasture. However, looking downstream, mature trees on the right bank of the river do screen the main road and the housing, and also the electricity substation, at least to some extent. However, the overhead wires leading to the substation dominate the view of the skyline looking upstream.

Looking downstream, the horizon is dominated by the ring-road bridge and causeway, although they are some distance away, and trees do break up the view. Across the flood plain, a developing copse hides the pump-house, and recently planted trees to the north-east are gradually softening the view.

The river is rather straight and regimented upstream of the footbridge, with no scrub or trees on the left bank, which was recently dredged and

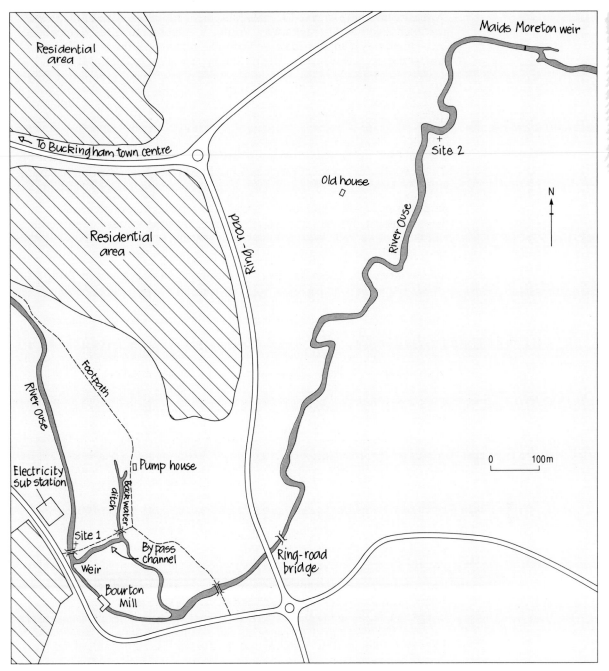

Figure 2.4   Map of River Ouse, Buckingham showing location of Sites 1 and 2

reformed. The bypass channel running north-east across the flood plain from the collapsed weir to join the backwater ditch is more attractive, especially near the weir, where a wide pool and shallow gravel area provide variety. Again though, this is totally devoid of all bankside vegetation except **ruderals** and grasses.

Downstream of the ring-road, the landscape is more open, and the horizons are much lower and further away. From a viewpoint along the river's edge at the main meander upstream of Maids Moreton weir, the general impression is one of spacious calm. The river here is relatively slack and deep, retained by the level of the weir crest, with only occasional shallower gravel beds. Again, the river banks are an indistinct feature, lacking the presence of bankside trees. However, the river is the central corridor around which the landscape spreads.

Although woodland is largely absent, a thickset old hedge with hawthorns and ash trees forms a positive boundary on the north side. An old house on the (now filled in) canal appears as an isolated rural homestead in harmony with the surrounding fields, in contrast to the housing estates just upstream.

Bankside emergent vegetation is better developed and more conspicuous than upstream, the shelves of bur-reed and club-rush forming identifiable blocks of colour and texture along the river edge. Similarly, in the shallower areas of water, flowering beds of water-crowfoot midstream catch the eye.

A summary of the landscape features for Sites 1 and 2 is given in Table 2.3.

Table 2.3 Checklist of landscape features: landform, vegetation and structures for the River Ouse, Buckingham

	Site 1 Bourton Mill	Site 2 Maids Moreton
LANDFORM	River *** Ditch * Stream * Broad valley **	River *** Broad valley *** Ditch * Lowland **
SLOPES	Gently sloping ** Flat **	Gently sloping *** Flat ***
VEGETATION	Flood meadow *** Hedgerows *** River banks *** Groups of trees (broad-leaved) *** Improved pasture *** Woodland fringe ** Roadside verges *	Improved pasture *** Hedgerows *** River banks *** Groups of trees (broad-leaved) *** Arable ** Woodland fringe ** Isolated trees ***
STRUCTURES	Buildings *** Electricity wires/pylons *** Fences *	Buildings * Pylons * Fences *

ASSESSMENT OF WET HABITATS

Habitat assessment, as described in Chapter 3 of the foundation book, requires some understanding of the relationships between species and their habitats. It is also useful to be able to name the plants and animals that you find in a habitat (using the many, widely available field guides), to understand how they are likely to react to changes in the habitat and to recognise the signs that suggest that an area may be particularly valuable for wildlife. This chapter provides more detail on the assessment of water and wetland habitats using the criteria of naturalness, diversity, rarity and size.

3.1   Water and wetland ecology

The value of a wet habitat for wildlife depends on many factors, such as age, size, depth, nutrient levels and water chemistry, and the relationship of the habitat to other habitats. Interactions between these factors and the ecological processes that occur over time are primarily responsible for the types of plant and animal communities present in a particular habitat. These interactions and ecological processes are summarised in Figures 3.1 and 3.2 (overleaf) for 'typical' still, open water and peat bog ecosystems. The arrows indicate the flow of energy and/or organic material within the water or wetland communities and their relative thickness indicates the extent of the influence on the ecosystem.

Ecological processes in the aquatic environment

Each individual body of water or wetland offers slightly different conditions for plants and animals to live in. The variety of wet habitats is enormous, and so is the variety of plant and animal species potentially associated with them. Variety is a good indicator of the 'health' of a habitat. If there are a lot of different species, this indicates a well-balanced, thriving ecosystem, but if only a few are present, this could suggest an imbalance of some sort, which prevents the survival of less tolerant species.

Fresh water is one of the richest wildlife environments in Great Britain. The list of animals known to occur in fresh water contains approximately 3800 species, of which nearly 2000 are insects. Insects and other **invertebrates** are very useful when assessing the wildlife value of freshwater habitats, because of their enormous variety and distribution. Within the total number of species there are of course considerable differences in the pattern of distribution of each species. Many species will only be found in certain geographical regions, depending on climate and morphology. Others may be distributed widely, but only be found in specific habitat conditions, such as still water or fast-flowing, stony-bottomed streams or unpolluted waters.

Diversity of plants and animals is an important concept, both within a habitat as well as between habitats. For example, a natural river habitat will include riffles and pools, which provide different environmental conditions and which will be inhabited by different communities of plants and animals. It is therefore not sufficient in terms of conserving wildlife simply to conserve a river, the variations of habitat within it must also be conserved.

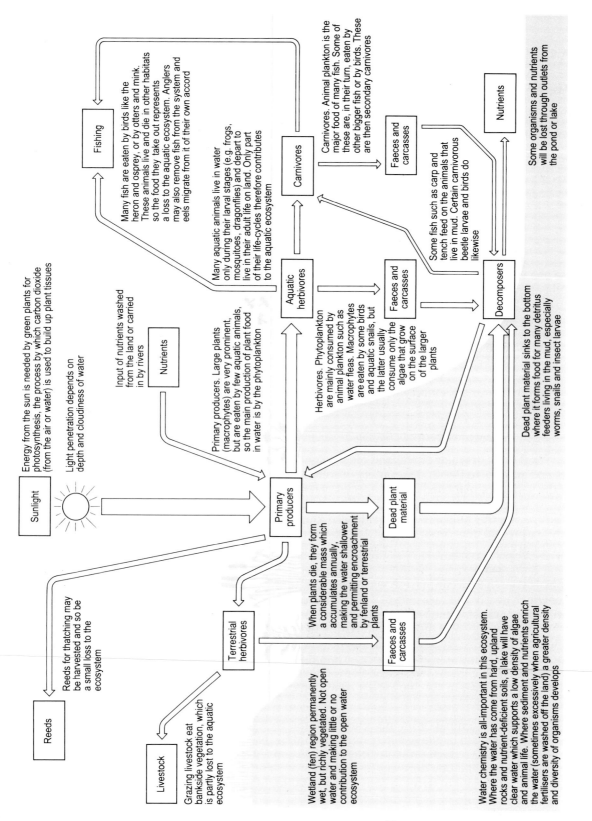

Figure 3.1   The ecosystem of ponds and lakes. (Source: After Morris, 1980)

29

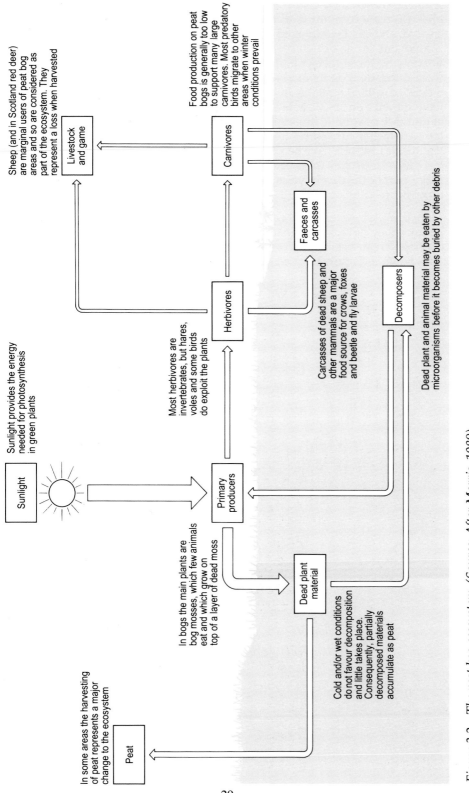

Figure 3.2   The peat bog ecosystem. (Source: After Morris, 1980)

Sunlight provides the energy needed for photosynthesis in green plants

Sunlight

Primary producers

In bogs the main plants are bog mosses, which few animals eat and which grow on top of a layer of dead moss

Dead plant material

Cold and/or wet conditions do not favour decomposition and little takes place. Consequently, partially decomposed materials accumulate as peat

In some areas the harvesting of peat represents a major change to the ecosystem

Peat

Most herbivores are invertebrates, but hares, voles and some birds do exploit the plants

Herbivores

Carnivores

Livestock and game

Sheep (and in Scotland red deer) are marginal users of peat bog areas and so are considered as part of the ecosystem. They represent a loss when harvested

Food production on peat bogs is generally too low to support many large carnivores. Most predatory birds migrate to other areas when winter conditions prevail

Faeces and carcasses

Carcasses of dead sheep and other mammals are a major food source for crows, foxes and beetle and fly larvae

Decomposers

Dead plant and animal material may be eaten by microorganisms before it becomes buried by other debris

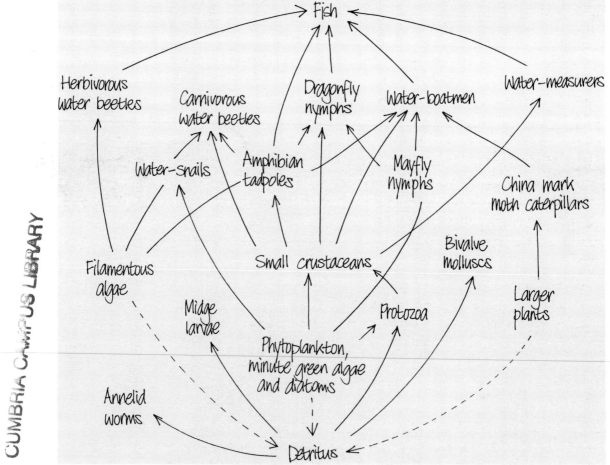
Complex relationships exist between the plants and animals of any ecosystem. The simple food chain – **carnivore** eats **herbivore** eats plant – is multiplied to create complex food webs. A balanced system of interdependence is created, and can be damaged or destroyed by disturbance to any individual component. If one or two species of plant or animal are reduced in number, not only do those species suffer, but also those that feed upon them and all those dependent on them via the food web. Studies of dippers, a bird characteristic of upland streams, in the upper reaches of the River Wye in Wales have shown a strong correlation between their breeding success and the abundance of aquatic invertebrates, particularly certain types of caddis fly larvae, which in turn correlates with the acidity of the water. There is evidence that the **headwaters** have become increasingly acidic in recent decades, and this has caused a decline in the numbers of caddis fly larvae, which constitute a major part of the diet of young dippers. Consequently, the number of dippers breeding successfully in these waters has declined.

More complex systems can withstand disturbance better than simple ones, because they have some capacity to buffer any change. In other words, diversity creates stability. For example, fish at the top of a food web, like the one shown in Figure 3.3, feed on a variety of aquatic invertebrates and will

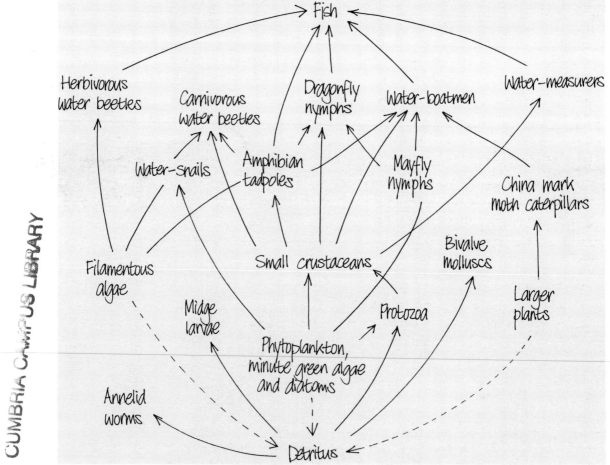

Figure 3.3   Food web of a pond. (Dashed lines indicate breaking-down process.)
(Source: Adapted from Clegg, 1974)

adapt their diet to the loss of a particular species by eating slightly more of the others. Overall, the effects on the other species in the web would be quite small, and balance would easily be restored.

In the management planning process, it is important to remember that wetlands are constantly changing systems. A pond or lake will change as the succession of vegetation proceeds. Rooted plants, such as reeds, accumulate silt between their stems, and as they die and decompose the bottom sediment becomes thicker and thicker and the depth of the water decreases. This allows other plants to establish root holds further and further into what was open water. Plants such as sedges, willow and alder grow where the reeds were, and eventually the whole area is converted from open water through a succession of marsh to fen to carr to woodland and dry land. This would inevitably lead to a reduction in the diversity of habitats available for the plants and animals. Maintaining an area of open water of sufficient depth to restrict the encroachment of water's edge vegetation, and control of the growth of scrub and bushes in the drier areas, will provide the best variety of habitats.

Waterways have a very important ecological role in the dispersal of species and colonisation of new habitats by both plants and animals. With the decline in wet habitats across the country, many water and wetland areas are now separated from other similar environments by miles of what is, effectively, desert. Canals, rivers, streams and ditches can be very important as corridors along which species can disperse to reach new areas, or to recolonise places that have been ecologically damaged in the past but have now recovered.

Plants propagate either by seed or vegetatively (that is, when a part of the plant is broken off, usually the root or stem, it is capable of growing into a new plant). In either case, it is necessary to retain some mature plants to allow the processes of regeneration to take place. Consequently, any cutting back or removal of overgrown vegetation should always leave some areas untouched, so that the plants can recover from the disturbance and the previous diversity can be maintained.

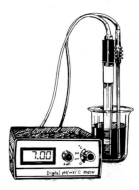

Water chemistry

The quality of fresh water is determined by its physical and chemical characteristics. Several of these are a function of the geographical location of the waterway concerned, the local geology and the general lie of the land. These underlying factors cause the natural variation in water quality that occurs throughout the country.

In general, the upland areas of Great Britain lie in the north and west, where the rocks are harder. The typical stream or river of the uplands is fast flowing and turbulent, with a rocky or stony bottom and clear water. The water will probably be cool, and it will be well oxygenated, because turbulence increases contact between the water and the atmosphere. Upland streams are generally colonised by plants and animals that have the ability to cling on tightly to the **substrate**, and that require good levels of **dissolved oxygen**.

Lowland streams and rivers tend to be slower moving, with a sandy or muddy bottom. Their temperature is likely to be higher and oxygen levels lower. The river water will be a combination of waters from different tributaries, and is likely to have a greater load of **suspended solids**, increasing its **turbidity**.

31

There are other chemical differences between typical upland and lowland streams, which may not be visible, because they are due to the substances dissolved in the water. Upland streams tend to be more acidic than lowland waters, due to the natural presence of organic acids. The acidity or alkalinity is expressed as the **pH** of the water. Most living things require an environment with a pH around neutral, although some have a narrower range of tolerance than others. A certain tolerance to pH variation is, in fact, essential to aquatic species, as the pH of freshwater habitats varies daily and seasonally in response to plant **photosynthesis**, which alters the carbon dioxide levels in the water.

Photosynthesis can only take place during daylight hours; this not only causes fluctuating levels of carbon dioxide but, more significantly, of dissolved oxygen. **Respiration** by animals, plants and bacteria in the water depletes the dissolved oxygen – a process that continues for 24 hours a day. This can create severe problems for aquatic life, as the only input of oxygen apart from photosynthesis is surface aeration. In flowing water, particularly turbulent watercourses, oxygenation from the atmosphere is very significant, but at the surface of a still pond the exchange of gases is limited. During the night, a thickly vegetated pond may become almost depleted of oxygen, which only slowly builds up again during the day. The effect is exacerbated in warm weather, as cool water is capable of holding more oxygen in solution than the same volume of warm water.

The **hardness** of water is determined by the type of rock that the water flows through and over. Hardness is caused by the presence of carbonates and bicarbonates of calcium and magnesium in the water. Calcium is usually the more abundant. It is derived from lime-bearing rocks and soils, which include chalk and other limestones and also marl and some basalt. Water plants, like any other plant, have different lime requirements, so different species may prefer hard or soft waters. Similarly, some snails and **crustaceans** are only found in very hard waters, because they need calcium to build their shells or external skeletons respectively. Freshwater sponges, on the other hand, cannot tolerate very hard water.

Another important aspect of water chemistry is the quantity of plant nutrients dissolved in the water and their effect on biological productivity. The most important of these are nitrates and phosphates, and their quantities will depend on the geology and land use within the catchment area. In regions with hard, insoluble rocks, the streams and ponds tend to have low nutrient levels, that is they are **oligotrophic**. In lowland Britain, the rock is generally softer and more soluble, and there is a consequent increase in the levels of nitrates and phosphates found naturally. Fresh water with high nutrient levels is called **eutrophic**. A medium level of nutrient status or productivity is described as **mesotrophic**.

Pollution

Pollution is a major culprit in the loss of wet habitats for wildlife. Streams and rivers have always been convenient pathways for the removal of wastes from human activities and they have suffered greatly as a result.

In polluted waters, sensitive species disappear, but others that are capable of tolerating the polluted water may thrive. This distorts the diverse population of clean waters, producing a situation with far fewer species, each of which may be found in large numbers. The reduction in numbers of species breaks down the complex relationships of the food web, thereby diminishing the quality of the entire ecosystem. In severely polluted water, hardly any living things can survive.

Pollution can be classified into various types, depending on the source of the pollutant and its effects on plants, animals and their environment (see Table 3.1).

Table 3.1 Pollution and water

Pollution	Sources	Effects
Organic matter	Sewage effluent; animal wastes; silage liquor; food processing waste	Dissolved oxygen removed from water; sensitive species cannot survive
Particulate material	Any disturbance of soil or rock; mining; sewage effluent; some industrial wastes; road run-off	Smothering of all plants and animals; reduced light penetration; filter feeders cannot feed
Acidification	Acid rain; air pollution; afforestation	Reduction in pH; sensitive species cannot survive
Toxic substances	Industrial wastes; pesticides	Death or sickness of sensitive species
Plant nutrients (nitrate and phosphate)	Fertiliser run-off; sewage effluent	Eutrophication

Organic matter is broken down or decomposed by the action of bacteria that use it as food. These naturally occurring bacteria also require oxygen to survive, and if the organic matter is in water, the bacteria will take the oxygen that they need from that dissolved in the water. This obviously has a damaging effect on the aquatic animals that depend on the dissolved oxygen to respire. Large quantities of organic matter in water may cause total deoxygenation, thus preventing almost all species of invertebrate and higher animals from surviving.

Organic matter

Particulate material suspended in the water usually presents different problems. If the turbidity of the water is increased by suspended solids, sunlight cannot penetrate more than a few centimetres below the surface, and plants will be unable to photosynthesise. Animals also suffer, because many aquatic species are filter feeders, that is they remove microscopic fragments of food from the water that moves past them. If the water is full of non-food particles, their feeding systems become clogged and they die.

Particulate material

Acidification of natural waters is an increasing problem, especially in uplands where the water is already acidic. Many lakes in Europe have been found to have a pH so reduced that hardly any life survives. The major cause is acid rain created by burning fossil fuels, but other factors have also been implicated, such as afforestation of uplands (see Box 4.1 in Section 4.3 of the foundation book).

Acidification

There are also a great many chemical pollutants that are directly toxic to plants or animals, which, if released into the environment, can cause catastrophic and possibly permanent destruction. Accidental spillage and thoughtless disposal of pesticides have caused many pollution incidents of this type. Other toxic substances may not have an acute effect, but can cause chronic and possibly cumulative damage to living organisms. There are many instances where industrial chemicals are regularly discharged into rivers and may have a long-term effect.

Toxic substances

The process of enrichment with plant nutrients or eutrophication is a natural one, but it is also a widespread form of water pollution from artificial sources, to the extent that natural variation becomes insignificant in comparison. It might seem that an increase in plant nutrients would be a good thing, as a greater number of plants and hence dependent animals could be supported. Unfortunately, this only applies up to a point. A mesotrophic pond would indeed be more productive than an oligotrophic one. However, as eutrophication progresses, certain species, particularly some algae, tend to dominate at the expense of others. The water turns green with the mass of microscopic algae, shading light from all plants and animals beneath the surface. When conditions change, for example at the end of the summer, the algal population crashes, and as the algae decay, oxygen is removed from the water, to the further detriment of the aquatic life.

Water level

For all water and wetland habitats, lack of water is bound to be, at the very least, severely damaging. Lowering of the **water table** by laying land drains and the deepening of drainage channels has occurred all over Britain, for the sake of improved productivity, ease of cultivation and flood protection. Innumerable ponds have been destroyed because they are no longer needed or are in the way of new development. Many others have been lost simply as a result of neglect, as succession takes place and they dry up, because maintaining them requires too much effort and serves no apparent purpose to the landowner.

For marshes, **peatlands** and other wetlands, the effects of a small change in the water table may be more subtle, but almost as damaging as completely drying up. A change of only a few centimetres can destroy the delicate balance of wetland flora, as many of these plants have particular requirements for depth of water and its seasonal fluctuation. Several very rare plants, including the legally protected brown galingale and adder's tongue spearwort, survive in and around the margins of shallow pools that dry out in summer.

It is an over-simplification to think only of the water level where it occurs above ground. There is a complex relationship between surface water, soil water and **groundwaters**, which will be affected by any alteration to the **hydrological system**. Before initiating any action that is likely to affect the system, possible 'knock-on' effects in other parts of the catchment area and beyond should be taken into account. For instance, if land drains are laid beneath a field that is inclined to be wet in winter, there will not necessarily be a loss of water from that field alone. The sub-surface water in adjacent fields will move towards a new level of equilibrium and the water table could be lowered over a much larger area than that of the new drains. In addition, the pattern of water content in ditches and streams around the field will be altered, which will affect plants and animals living there. The presence of the drains will make the effects of a rain shower more acute. The water will drain into the ditches more quickly than if it had percolated through the soil, and the resulting surge of water will be higher, which could have catastrophic effects on bankside plants and burrowing animals.

If a water supply is abstracted from groundwater by pumping from wells, this too may have damaging effects elsewhere in the catchment area. There is a **draw-down** of the water table around each well, and if several wells are sited together or if pumping is excessive, the drying out and permanent disappearance of springs and streams can result. There have been several examples of this, particularly in south-east England, such as the River Misbourne in Hertfordshire and the River Darent in Kent.

The extent of the area over which 'knock-on' effects may be felt is not easy to predict, as it is a function of many factors, including local geology, geomorphology, land use and climate.

Particular seasonal fluctuations in water level are essential to some types of wetland for their continued existence. **Water meadows** are a traditional form of agriculture, which depend on the management of water level by controlled seasonal flooding through sluice gates and channels. They are now extremely rare, because agricultural practices have changed, and improved drainage and the use of artificial fertiliser on pasture have made the water meadow regime inappropriate. A few are maintained in Hampshire and Dorset for their wildlife value.

Similarly, flood meadows and **washlands** adjacent to rivers depend on a cycle of fluctuating water level, although unlike water meadows this is not controlled by people. Particular plant communities develop in response to the pattern of occasional inundation, but these have become more rare as fewer rivers are allowed a natural flow regime.

Bank erosion can be a major problem on rivers, canals and larger lakes. Some bank erosion is quite usual on rivers, and under natural conditions is controlled to a large extent by the bankside vegetation. The roots of the plants hold the soil together and maintain the bank's stability. A problem arises if the equilibrium of this natural process is interfered with. Bankside vegetation may be removed, either to increase the area of land available for agricultural use or simply in a misguided attempt to 'tidy' the landscape. The stability is then lost and the bank can erode away at an alarming rate. It may become necessary to build an artificial bank support simply to re-establish the former stability.

Bank erosion

3.2   *Freshwater species*

The numbers and types of plant and animal species found in water and wetlands change with the seasons and over the years. They are the most visible evidence of the condition of a wet habitat and need to be monitored carefully.

Habitat requirements

If you are planning to undertake water and wetland management or creation you may already have some idea of the type of wildlife that you want to encourage. An understanding of the habitat requirements of the different types of plants and animals is necessary for effective planning. Many different factors combine to determine which species you can expect to colonise the area concerned. Some of these factors will be outside your control, such as your geographical location, but others you will be able to influence towards achieving your objectives. These are the physical features of the site, which can be manipulated to achieve particular site conditions. For example, the depth of water, the profile of the bank and the type of vegetation can all be managed in order to provide the habitat or range of habitats required by the species of plants and animals that you wish to encourage. This may not guarantee the success of these species, but it can at least improve their chances.

35

Which plants grow where in an aquatic ecosystem is determined to a large extent by the depth of the water. Other factors are also important, namely water turbulence and the type of substrate, as well as shading, slope, water quality and aspect. These factors will all influence the distribution of water plants, but the preferred depth of water is usually the dominant factor. This means that there are different zones of aquatic vegetation associated with different depths of water. The zones of a lowland pond are shown in Figure 3.4, and some of the plants that typify each zone are given in Table 3.2. Similar zonation will be seen at the edges of most ponds, lakes and rivers, although one or several of the zones may be missing, depending on the local conditions, and distinctions between zones are seldom clear.

Table 3.2 Pond plant zones – some typical species

Zone 1 Plants living in the marshy area some distance from the water

Marsh marigold; purple loosestrife; rushes; great willowherb; yellow flag; sedges; meadowsweet; water forget-me-not

Zone 2 Plants living in swampy conditions at the edge of the water, i.e. growing 'with their feet wet'

Common reed; bur-reeds; flowering rush; great reedmace; water-plantain; bogbean; bulrush (club-rush)

Zone 3 Plants rooted in the mud in shallow water at the pond margins, but having leaves either floating on the surface or standing out of the water

White water-lily; water-crowfoot; broad-leaved pondweed; yellow water-lily; arrowhead

Zone 4 Plants floating freely at the surface, not attached to the bottom

Duckweeds; water soldier; frogbit; bladderworts

Zone 5 Plants in deeper water, rooted in the mud with their vegetation completely submerged

Canadian pondweed; starworts; water-milfoil; hornworts; pondweeds

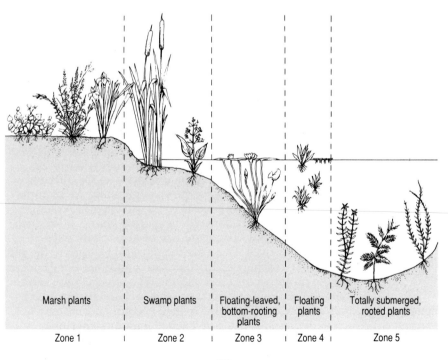

Figure 3.4   Profile of a pond margin showing zones of vegetation. (Source: Clegg, 1974)

Marsh plants	Swamp plants	Floating-leaved, bottom-rooting plants	Floating plants	Totally submerged, rooted plants
Zone 1	Zone 2	Zone 3	Zone 4	Zone 5

The plant communities of marshes, fens and bogs will include some of the species found in Zones 1, 2 and 3 of the truly aquatic systems as well as others specific to the particular conditions of the wetland. Table 3.3 lists some typical species of fen and bog.

Table 3.3 Typical fen and bog species

Fen

Grasses: Purple small-reed; reed canary-grass; reed sweet-grass

Herbs: Marsh cinquefoil; meadowsweet; ragged robin; reedmace; rushes; sedges; water avens; water mint; yellow flag

Shrubs/trees: Alder, willows

Bog

Bog asphodel; bog mosses; cotton-grass; cross-leaved heath; purple moor-grass; sedges; sundews

Mosses and algae are important members of aquatic plant communities, which should not be overlooked. Bog mosses are the definitive plants of bogs, as well as being found in many damp places at the edges of streams and ponds. Algae are a large group of non-flowering plants, which includes seaweeds and many plants growing in damp places on land and in fresh water. Many algae are microscopic, single-cell plants, which may occur in large numbers. The green layer on damp tree bark is a layer of algae, and other algal species are responsible for the green colour of the water of still pools. In fresh water there are also larger types of algae, which can dominate the aquatic environment. In some species, the cells are joined end to end to form a thread or filament. These filamentous algae can grow into huge masses and can clog a whole pond, particularly in the summer months. Problems may arise because the dense blanket of vegetation that these algae can produce prevents the growth of other plants. In addition, at night when photosynthesis ceases, the water can be severely deoxygenated by the mass of vegetation, to the detriment of aquatic animals. A further disadvantage is that, at the end of the growing season, the algae die off and decay, causing further deoxygenation and an unpleasant smell. Filamentous algae tend to be a problem in still, nutrient-rich water in an open, sunny position, where they can become dominant at the expense of other plants.

The phenomenon of 'algal blooms' is caused by microscopic green or blue-green algae. Algal blooms are most likely to occur in ponds or lakes with eutrophic water in summer, when the water is warmer and the sunlight hours greater. When conditions are good for the algae, they are capable of very rapid multiplication, which can turn the water to a dense, murky green colour within days or hours. The disadvantages are similar to those described above, that is deoxygenation and poor penetration of light below the surface to underwater plants. Some species of blue-green algae produce poisonous substances, which may kill aquatic animals including fish, and can be harmful to livestock, people, wild animals and birds if they come into close contact with the water. The control of excessive growths of algae is not easy, as the sources of the high nutrient levels producing them are often diffuse and difficult to pinpoint.

There are thousands of species of aquatic invertebrates found in Britain, amongst which will be some adapted to virtually every possible habitat condition. Some can live in a wide range of habitats and therefore have a

Invertebrates

37

wide distribution, others are limited by specific requirements of food, water quality, substrate, turbulence, temperature, water hardness, and so on. Still or sluggish water will typically support a different community from a fast-flowing stream, where the invertebrates must cling to stones or vegetation and find crevices for protection. Some species require a muddy substrate to live in, others need sand or light gravel in which to bury themselves, others stones or rocks on which they can graze.

The presence of vegetation is very important to invertebrates. A great many species use underwater plants to shelter in, as a source of food and for anchorage. Generally, there will be a greater variety of species found amongst the weed of a pond than in the bottom mud or open water (see Figure 3.5).

Some insect species, such as dragonflies, which spend their immature stages under water, depend on the presence of emergent plants to gain access to the air when they go through metamorphosis to the adult, flying stage.

Pollution is severely damaging to invertebrate communities. The more sensitive species will be unable to survive in even very slightly polluted water. Other species, which can tolerate contaminated conditions, may thrive and be found in abundance, but the diversity of species will be lost.

The mobility of most invertebrate species means that depth of water is not as critical for them as it is for water plants, although complete loss of water is obviously something that few will survive.

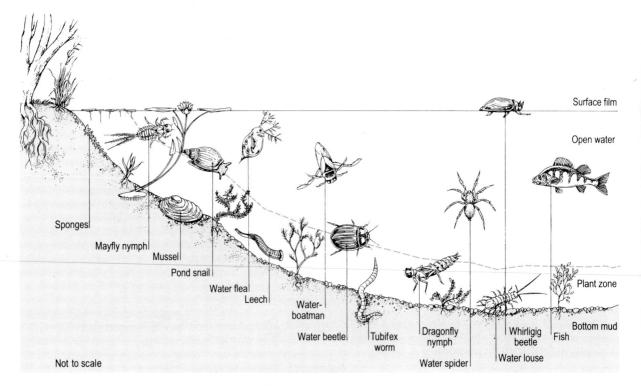

Figure 3.5   Pond zones and typical animals. (Source: Clegg, 1974)

38

There are only six native amphibian species in Britain: the great crested or warty newt, the smooth newt, the palmate newt, the common frog, the common toad and the natterjack toad, of which the first and last are very rare and protected. They all need water for breeding, but spend considerable parts of their lives on land. Generally, they prefer still, warm, shallow water, and so are more likely to be found in ponds than streams or rivers. As they develop, the tadpoles go through a herbivorous stage before becoming carnivores, so both aquatic plants and invertebrates are essential for their success. Once they are mature, they leave the water and move away from the pond. They prefer ponds that have vegetation growing around them, such as long grass or low-growing scrubby plants, as this provides habitat for food organisms and good cover from some predators.

Amphibians have declined in numbers, largely due to habitat loss. In addition, the construction of buildings, roads and other developments can prevent frogs and toads from returning to their spawning grounds, and the removal of spawn for a tank on the school nature table is another, not insignificant, means of loss. The good intentions behind pond clearance work can also be damaging. Tadpoles may be found from March to November, so any dredging or clearance work during this period should be avoided, but digging out silted-up ponds or pond surrounds in winter can kill hibernating adults. One solution is to clear only one-quarter or one-third of a pond in any one year.

The two basic requirements for fish are adequate oxygen and adequate food. Other important habitat features include water velocity, substrate material, temperature, turbidity and the availability of cover provided by vegetation or overhanging banks. Each species has its own particular requirements, although some are much fussier than others.

British freshwater fish can be divided into two main groups: salmonids (game fish) and coarse fish. Anglers would separate a third group of small coarse fish, such as minnow, bullhead, stoneloach and stickleback. Salmonids, i.e. salmon, trout and grayling, have more demanding habitat requirements than the others. They require moderate- to fast-flowing, cool water with a gravelly bottom for spawning and clean, unpolluted water with a relatively high dissolved oxygen content. In their natural condition, they are found in the cool, turbulent waters of coastal streams or upland reaches of larger rivers. Trout also live in lakes, but only where the water temperature never exceeds 20°C and the dissolved oxygen level does not fall too low. Coarse fish are typically found in warmer, less turbulent lowland reaches, and also in canals, ponds and lakes. This group includes eel, dace, chub, barbel, perch, pike, roach, rudd, bream, tench and carp. They can tolerate fairly wide temperature fluctuations, and some, such as carp, can survive in quite polluted water with a relatively low dissolved oxygen content. Coarse fish tend to have a more varied diet, and can use invertebrates, plants and detritus as food. The presence of bankside and aquatic vegetation is important, as it can provide food, both in itself and in the invertebrates that live around it, and also protection from predators and shading from sunlight.

The birds seen on and around any water body or wetland area are one of the major wildlife attractions of these habitats. As well as the truly aquatic species, the majority of British birds can be seen near water within their range at some time of the year. The increasing popularity of birdwatching has been responsible for the protection and creation of many water habitats.

The major requirements for water birds include access to water, shelter from predators, weather and general disturbance, appropriate sources of food and availability of nesting sites for breeding species. In addition, the surrounding land should have mixed vegetation, including trees, scrub and long and short grasses, as diversity of vegetation will encourage different species of bird.

Water birds can be divided by their feeding habits into two main groups: dabblers and divers. Dabblers have a diet that includes a large proportion of vegetable matter; in this group are mallard, pintail and teal. Divers, such as tufted duck and great crested grebe, eat fish, aquatic invertebrates and, in some cases, weed. Dabblers prefer water depths between 15 centimetres and 2 metres, but divers need slightly greater depths, from 60 centimetres to 2.5 metres or more.

Wading birds, such as heron and common sandpiper, require shallow areas for feeding. Other species, such as wigeon and geese, feed by grazing on grassland, so they prefer sloping, grassed banks as feeding grounds.

Water bodies and wetlands are also important feeding grounds for insectivorous birds. Clouds of midges, gnats and mosquitoes over water provide rich pickings for swallows and martins in the summer.

Even if the particular habitat requirements of a bird species are met, the geographical distribution of that species is of over-riding importance. The variations in climate and terrain across Britain dictate which species live and breed in any location, and so any habitat enhancement will inevitably be restricted by this distribution. Generally, a broad range of species will be encouraged by providing a variety of habitats. Conversely, if management is aimed at the conservation of one particular species, the particular habitat requirements of that species must be provided.

Mammals

Otter, water vole and water shrew are the only native aquatic mammals in Britain. Mink and coypu have been introduced in the past and mink are now well established, but efforts to eradicate coypu have been successful and they are now believed to have been exterminated in the wild.

Otters need dense cover along the banks of their riverside territories. They use surface vegetation or bank cavities as holts for daytime refuge as well as breeding sites, and they use several holts along their extensive territories. Favoured holt locations are the root systems of mature trees in association with a dense undergrowth of bramble thickets, rhododendrons, gorse, hawthorn scrub or large beds of reed or sedge. It is the loss of bankside vegetation in the cause of tidying up watercourses that has made many locations unusable by otters. If they have adequate cover, they are surprisingly tolerant of human presence, although they dislike dogs, and any disturbance should be avoided if possible, as they are protected under the Wildlife and Countryside Act 1981.

Water shrews can be identified by their long, pointed snouts and small size. They feed during day and night on aquatic insects, small fish and amphibians, as well as land invertebrates. They live in tunnels in the banks of clear, slow streams and ponds and need bankside vegetation for protection from predators.

Water voles are brown and a similar size to rats, but have more rounded snouts and smaller ears. They are quite common throughout Britain on lowland rivers, canals, ponds and drainage ditches, and are often heard rather than seen as they dive into the water when footsteps approach. They are mainly vegetarian, feeding on grass and emergent aquatic plants, which also provide them with cover. They live in burrows dug into banks, with several entrance holes both above and below water level.

Two species of bat are particularly associated with rivers: Natterer's bat and Daubenton's bat. They require mature trees with cracks and hollow trunks as roost sites. They feed on insects flying over water and bankside vegetation.

3.3　Habitat and wildlife assessment criteria

With a basic understanding of water ecology, as described in Section 3.1, a detailed assessment of the wildlife habitat value of wet habitats can be made. This can never be truly 'objective', as there will always be situations where even experts will disagree, or cases where personal preferences have an important influence. In the foundation book, four criteria are offered as a guide to assessing the value of a habitat:

- its naturalness;
- its diversity;
- its rarity and the rarity of the species that it contains;
- its area or size.

As with landscape assessment, assessing the wildlife value of a habitat is best done by marking important areas on a map, taking photographs or making sketches from recorded positions and making detailed notes describing each area.

If the site has been designated, for example as an SSSI, detailed surveys will already have been made by professional naturalists from the Nature Conservancy Council and a copy given to the landowner. Even so, it is a good idea to do your own assessment, as you will learn more about the area, and be able to take a more constructive part in its management in the future.

Naturalness

The criterion of naturalness is intended to convey the extent to which a habitat is affected by the activities of humans. For the purposes of wet habitat assessment, naturalness can be equated to water quality.

As discussed earlier, there are many aspects of water quality – pH, particulate material, organic matter, inorganic compounds – that need specialist monitoring techniques, but there are a few simple signs that indicate the degree of pollution.

Pollution at its worst (whether from pesticide sprays, fertilisers, sewage, industrial effluent or even an excess of leaf material) is often indicated by such obvious evidence as dead fish floating on the surface of the water, oily slicks, foaming or scum.

Pollution can also be revealed by:

- vigorous growth of algae;
- evidence of partially decayed organic matter, for example accumulated leaves or animal excrement;

▶ cloudy water or change of colour (although some colouration is natural in waters from peaty soils);

▶ production of foul-smelling gases;

▶ the poor variety of plants and animals.

Rubbish is a problem common to all wet habitats, especially in urban areas. Its damaging effect on landscape value is mentioned in Chapter 2, but litter can be lethal to many animals. Tin cans, bottles, plastic bags and nylon fishing line are all potential deathtraps. Table 3.4 (p. 46) indicates how you can rate open water and wetlands for water quality. The ratings suggested are based on an assessment of water quality solely by visual characteristics. More detailed assessment of pollution using techniques of chemical analysis is possible, but requires specialist equipment, which may not be available.

For wetlands, an alternative indicator of naturalness is the water level. Wetlands are characterised by a fairly stable, high water level within the soil or ground material. Activities that affect this water level temporarily or permanently alter the natural state that supports particular wildlife communities. Land drainage of the wetland or of the surrounding area is the most likely cause of a fall in water level. If a drainage system is completely effective, the wetland ceases to exist. In some instances, drains may be inefficient, either because they were inadequately laid in the first place or because they have silted up over time, and in these circumstances a lost wetland habitat may be restored. Table 3.4 gives ratings for wetland areas based on the influence of drainage.

Diversity

Species diversity

Diversity is, in one sense, a measure of the richness of wildlife present. In many situations, the best indicator of a rich wildlife habitat is the presence of a large number of different species of plants and animals. If there is a diverse population, the habitat is thriving. If the environment is disturbed in some way, the less tolerant species will no longer be able to compete successfully and so will not survive, the diversity of species will be reduced and the habitat will be impoverished. Individual species may prosper and be found in great numbers, but the loss of diversity will indicate a loss of value as a wildlife habitat.

There are exceptions to this general rule. Reed beds typically consist of a stand of a single plant species, common reed, but they support many species that rely heavily on this particular environment, such as the reed warbler, the very rare bittern and many other water birds that seek shelter in the reed swamp.

As vegetation is a crucial part of any habitat, an assessment of plant species is always worth while. Look at the vegetation and see how many different plants you can find. Try to identify some with the aid of reference books (see Appendix I). You should include plants from a variety of situations, both above and below water. This may be easiest to achieve by working along an imaginary line or transect, taken at right angles to the water margin so that it crosses the site from the top of the bank down into the water, as far as wellington boots and common sense will allow. Do be prepared to go into the water, if it is not too deep, and paddle about. Examination of aquatic plants and animals is much easier if you are close to them, and you may obtain a new perspective from standing in the river looking out.

42

To examine the invertebrate population, you need a small-mesh net and a deep white tray. Put a little water from the pond or stream into the tray. Slowly sweep the net through the water a few times; this is best done through the submerged vegetation if there is any. Then invert the contents of the net into the tray and wash any debris off the net. You should see a variety of small creatures, wriggling, gliding and swimming around. Count how many different types you can see. It is not necessary to be able to name the species, merely be able to say that specimen A is different from specimen B and so on, although with the aid of a good reference book identification of some invertebrates is not too difficult. Repeat the procedure a few times in different locations, including a sample of the bottom mud. Remember to put the animals back in the water when you have finished. Do not forget the adult insects that may be found in association with the wet habitat. Dragon-flies and damselflies will often be seen flying over ponds and streams on warm, summer days.

Structural diversity

Structural diversity is especially important at the edge of open water where a gradually shelving bank and varied depth of water can provide opportunities for many types of aquatic plants (see Figure 3.4). Very steep sides and very deep waters do not make a good open water habitat, because both severely limit the vegetation that can grow. An irregular, indented water margin adds further to structural diversity by creating small **bays** and **spits** along the water's edge, as well as extending the total length of the valuable shallow water zone.

To measure the depth of open water, you can use a marked pole, a broom or net handle, or, if convenient, a weighted line. In a lake or large pond this is best done from a boat, but leaning out (with care) from the bank may well be the only option, in which case the maximum depth will have to be an educated guess. Be aware of the dangers of deep water and be very cautious when leaning out from a bank to measure depth, or when wading into the water.

The pattern of depth over an area can be important, so if possible take readings in several places. The depth is very likely to change with the seasons of the year, so remember that the conditions you see at a particular moment may vary. The depth of still waters is also affected by the accumulation of silt and organic matter.

For wetlands, species diversity ratings are only suggested for plants, as assessing invertebrate diversity would be too problematic. The concept of structural diversity is generally less applicable to wetlands and so it too is excluded from the suggested criteria. There are exceptions to this, for example a marshy area may be enhanced by the presence of small pools of open water, providing a more diverse habitat.

Table 3.4 shows how open water can be rated for species and structural diversity.

Rarity

To find out whether you have a rare and/or protected species of plant or animal on your land requires precise identification. You may wish to tackle this exercise yourself, but it is probably not necessary to get too bogged down in the anatomical details of, for example, sedges or water-boatmen, unless, of course, you want to do so.

Plants do have the advantage of staying in one place while you look at them, but many groups are difficult to identify unless you are an expert. With animals, there may be difficulties in seeing them at all, before confronting the problems of identification.

For amphibia, the best time to observe the adults is at dusk in spring; also, spawn is visible in the water at this time of year. Correct identification of the great crested newt is essential because of its protected status.

Assessment techniques for fish may be simply watching and noting their presence. In appropriate circumstances, you may be able to make use of anglers' records of catches or, in artificially stocked waters, of the records of the fishery manager.

Birds are relatively easy to observe and identify. Take time to sit quietly and watch, with binoculars if possible.

Mammals are more elusive, and you are unlikely to obtain more than a glimpse of them, although evidence of their presence may be easier to spot. Only the otter, the water vole and the water shrew actually require open water for their existence, but many other British mammals will make use of water and be occasional visitors if they are present in the vicinity.

If you get stuck with identification or have limited time or inclination, you may find other people willing to help, for example the local Wildlife Trust, school or college.

Many of Britain's rarest and endangered species are solely dependent on specific wet habitats, and are extremely vulnerable to a reduction in quality or quantity of those particular habitats, e.g. the natterjack toad, the otter, the marsh harrier, the bittern, the bladderwort, the sundew.

If you suspect that you have found or seen a rare species, especially if it is on the protected list of the Wildlife and Countryside Act 1981 (see the *Legislation and Regulations* booklet in the foundation module), you should contact the Nature Conservancy Council for advice, as you will be breaking the law if you disturb it or its environment.

Area

If a piece of open water or wetland is rated highly for naturalness, diversity and/or species rarity, then generally, the bigger the area, the better its wildlife value. Area is particularly important to those species that need large territories to provide them with enough food, e.g. otters and kingfishers. Not only is the size of an individual site important, but also the proximity of similar sites, which may enable recolonisation if one site suffers a severe disturbance.

The measurement of surface area of ponds and lakes may be difficult, unless this can be derived from existing maps. In fact, because much of the wildlife is situated at the water's edge, absolute area may not be as important as the extent of the water margins. These may be estimated by pacing around the perimeter, or possibly using a rope or land-tape. The length of water margin can be measured in a similar fashion for watercourses.

The other difficulty in using area as a criterion for habitat value is that increasing size does not necessarily mean increasing value. Some very small ponds or wetlands may have an extremely rich flora and fauna. If they are the last remnants of a larger habitat, they may provide havens for relict species which, given the opportunity, will be available to colonise new areas if and when they are created. For these reasons, specific ratings for area of open water are not suggested.

The size of a wetland site is more critical to its overall value as a wildlife habitat, since larger areas will be less vulnerable to external changes, such as the draining of adjacent land.

Ratings for wetland habitats on the basis of area are given in Table 3.4.

3.4   Overall wet habitat assessment

The four habitat assessment criteria described above overlap to some extent; a site that has a high score for one criterion is more likely to have a high score for the others and vice versa. However, they do not overlap completely; a site may have a high score for species diversity but a low score for rarity. Remember that the ratings are not quantitative and should not be treated as real numbers: a site that rates four stars on naturalness cannot be considered twice as good as one that rates two stars. Nor need you obtain a rating for each criterion if it is difficult, although the more you have the better.

Taken together, ratings of a water and wetland area using the checklist in Table 3.4 will provide an overview or profile of its habitat value and a basis for improving it. You can then look at individual or related criteria to see what can be done to improve them, without downgrading the site on the remaining criteria. The overall objectives should be to maintain those aspects of a site that are already highly rated, to enhance those that are of poor to moderate value and to create new features that will add to the value of the site.

3.5   Making your own water or wetland habitat assessment

As with landscape assessment, this is a more specific extension of the general habitat assessment described in Chapter 3 of the foundation book.

> Fill in a habitat assessment profile for the areas of water and wetland on your holding or study area, using Tables 3.5 and 3.6 (pp. 50, 51) as examples (fill in a separate profile for each distinct area if there is more than one). Include a map drawn at an appropriate scale to suit the site, and mark on it the major features of the site, particularly the vegetation type. Supplement this with more detail on the various habitat and wildlife assessment criteria, as suggested in Table 3.4 (overleaf).
>
> In addition, you should include notes on the water chemistry, if known, especially pH, hardness and any known pollutants. The type of substrate can also be significant, that is whether it is rock, stone, gravel, mud or sand.

Doesn't look like anything's colonised this pond, yet, Kevin..... Kevin?

You should bear in mind the timing of your assessment and try to repeat the procedure at different seasons of the year. If it is only possible to do this twice in the year, April/May and August/September are probably the best times, because most plants and animals will be active during the summer.

Table 3.4 Habitat assessment criteria for open water and wetlands

Criteria	Rating	Criteria	Rating

A Open water

1 Naturalness (water quality)

Unpolluted (no algae, clear water, no discolouration, no rubbish) 4*

Slightly polluted (few algae, slight discolouration, little organic matter, no rubbish) 3*

Moderately polluted (some algae, discolouration of water, some organic matter, some rubbish) 2*

Severely polluted (algae abundant, severe discolouration, much organic matter, some rubbish) 1*

2 Diversity

2.1 Plant species diversity per transect

>15 species 4*

11–15 species 3*

5–10 species 2*

< 5 species 1*

2.2 Invertebrate types

>15 types 4*

11–15 types 3*

5–10 types 2*

< 5 types 1*

2.3 Structural

Irregular, shelving banks, range of depths to 2 metres, little or no fluctuations in water level, indented margins 4*

Shelving edges but little range in depths, little change in water level, margin indented for some of its length 3*

Shelving edges but little range in depths, severe fluctuations of water level, generally straight margins 2*

Very steep regular banks, often shallow water, severely silted, straight margins 1*

3 Rarity of species

Containing one (or more) species of plant and/or animal that is nationally rare 4*

Containing one (or more) species of plant and/or animal that is locally or regionally rare 3*

Containing plant and/or animal species that are widespread, but restricted to water and wetland habitat 2*

Containing no species in any of the above categories 1*

B Wetlands

1 Naturalness

1.1 Water quality

Unpolluted clear water (no rubbish, no algae, no discolouration) 4*

Slightly polluted (no rubbish, few algae, some discolouration) 3*

Moderately polluted (some rubbish, some algae, some discolouration) 2*

Severely polluted (dirty water, some rubbish, dense algae) 1*

1.2 Drainage

Wetland site with no nearby drainage 4*

Wetland site with nearby drainage 3*

Wetland site with direct drainage, now ineffective 2*

Former wetland site with functioning drains 1*

2 Diversity

Plant species diversity per transect

>15 species 4*

11–15 species 3*

5–10 species 2*

< 5 species 1*

3 Rarity of species

Containing one (or more) species of plant and/or animal that is nationally rare 4*

Containing one (or more) species of plant and/or animal that is locally or regionally rare 3*

Containing plant and/or animal species that are widespread but restricted to water and wetland habitat 2*

Containing no species in any of the above categories 1*

4 Area

Vegetated areas greater than 10 ha 4*

Vegetated areas between 5 and 10 ha 3*

Vegetated areas between 1 and 5 ha 2*

Vegetated areas less than 1 ha 1*

However, this will not apply if, for example, your interest is in migratory birds that only visit in winter. Be prepared to add to and amend your assessment notes at a later date, and regularly in forthcoming seasons.

Some potential hazards associated with freshwater habitats, such as drowning, are obvious, so be appropriately cautious near deep water. If possible, do not go to a site alone, and at least tell someone else where you are going, what you are planning to do and when you expect to return. There are other less obvious dangers. Several diseases are spread by waterborne bacteria and viruses, and although the chances of infection are very small, you should wash your hands thoroughly after contact with the water.

Health and safety

3.6   Habitat assessment of case study areas

Please note that this cannot be comprehensive and concentrates on the major features.

Borders Farm

Pond and wetland features occupy over 6 of the 445 hectares of the farm (excluding the river and burns). Virtually all of these have been created by the current owner. Three of the pond and wetland features, designated Sites 1, 2 and 3, have been selected as examples for detailed habitat assessment. These features include:

▶ Site 1: Wetland with a series of half a dozen small pools created in a very wet mire area (for wildlife only)

▶ Site 2: One large pond for fishing (Mossbrae Lochan)

▶ Site 3: Two flight ponds in close proximity to each other

▶ One large pond for fishing and duck-flighting

▶ One large pond near to the house as a landscape feature and for some fishing

▶ One flight pond in isolation on the hill

▶ One large pond in a valley walk near the house

▶ One wetland area, which is now supplied with piped additional water to make it wetter (for wildlife only)

▶ Numerous wet flushes and water tracks over the hill land.

Figure 3.6 (overleaf) is a map of the farm showing the ponds and wetland areas as well as woodland and grassland habitats.

In all cases, the habitats have no extremely rare species, or even a necessarily high species diversity. It is hoped that these will come with time. It must be borne in mind that these are relatively new features, and colonisation is a slow process.

In creating these features, the most has been made of opportunities to create structural diversity. This is shown in the three selected examples. In the case of Sites 1 and 3, there is plenty of 'edge', shallow water and deep water. This gives a wide range of **niches** which plants may colonise. Site 2 is a much larger feature and, while 'edge' may not be well developed or particularly varied, the site does offer a large expanse of sheltered open water, which complements the other nearby habitats.

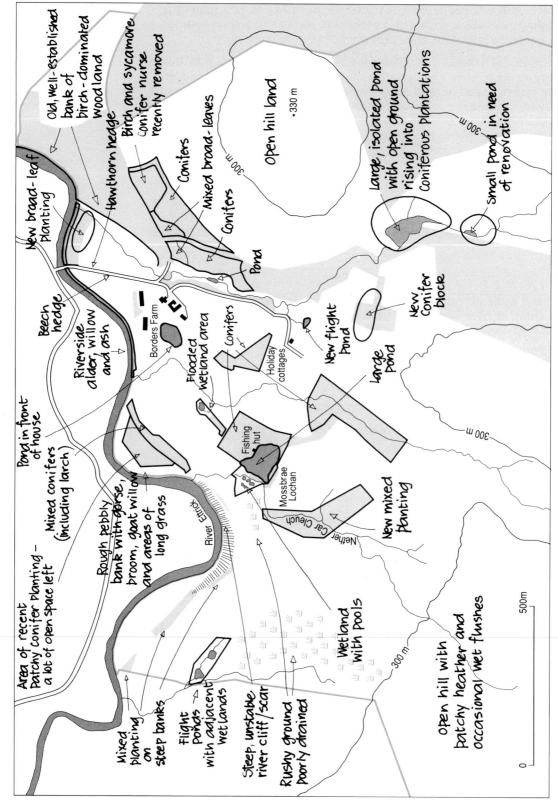

Area of recent
Patchy conifer planting –
a lot of open space left

Pond in front
of house

Mixed conifers
(including larch)

Old, well-established
bank of
birch-dominated
woodland

New broad-leaf
planting

Hawthorn hedge

Birch and sycamore,
conifer nurse
recently removed

Conifers

Mixed broad-leaves

Conifers

Pond

Open hill land

·330 m

300 m

Large, isolated pond
with open ground
rising into
coniferous plantations

300 m

Small pond in need
of renovation

Beech
hedge

Riverside alder, willow
and ash

Borders Farm

Flooded
wetland area

Conifers

Holiday
cottages

New flight
Pond

Large
Pond

New conifer
block

Fishing
hut

Mossbrae
Lochan

Nether Car Cleuch

New mixed
planting

300 m

Rough pebbly
bank with gorse,
broom, goat willow
and areas of
long grass

River Etterick

Mixed planting
on
steep banks

Flight
ponds
with adjacent
wetlands

Steep, unstable
river cliff/scar

Rushy ground
poorly drained

Wetland
with pools

300 m

open hill with
patchy heather and
occasional wet flushes

0   500m

Figure 3.6 Habitat assessment map of Borders Farm

The species that do occur provide the full range of aquatic plant diversity, occupying niches from the wetted fringe to deep, open water: soft rush, sharp-flowered rush, sedges, waterworts, bog pondweed, broad-leaved pondweed, lesser spearwort, flote-grass, water-crowfoot, cuckoo flower (lady's smock).

Invertebrate numbers reflect this structural diversity, and are supported by a clear, well-oxygenated water supply, although this is comparatively acidic and of low nutrient status.

Sited below the dam of Mossbrae Lochan, this wetland area receives water from direct surface flow and throughflow of groundwater. The site had been rough grazed, originally as a wet valley mire, with a relatively uniform character. The terracing and creation of ponds with a wide range of depths and edge profiles has given a feature of considerable diversity, playing host to a wider range of plant species than the original habitat. The feature attracts duck, snipe (and other occasional wading birds) and even pheasant.

Excavation by tracked machine was followed by hand placing of wetland turf from nearby, to inoculate effectively the new pools and to encourage rapid colonisation.

Broad-leaved trees (mainly alder and willow species) have been planted in small groups around the pools. Other additional trees have been placed in larger groups in the corners of the area, which is designated a conservation feature by the landowner. A habitat assessment profile is shown in Table 3.5 (overleaf).

This large pond was created as a landscape and recreational feature, but at the same time has much wildlife value, mainly due to the large expanse of open water.

Water is piped into the lochan from Nether Car Cleuch, and it is also fed by a variety of small burns flowing through the conifer plantation.

Shorelines are of three different characters.

▶ The north-east shore comprises an unusual curving dam with a reinforced stone rip-rap facing consisting of loose rocks placed securely on the slope of the dam above and below the normal water level. This reduces erosion as well as improving the colonisation potential for plants.

▶ The north-west shore has been opened up, with the thinning out of selected trees, to leave specimen trees with open, grassy areas and an excellent wet fringe, which provides good loafing for duck amongst emergent vegetation

▶ The south-west/southern shore is relatively dark, shaded and sheltered. Conifers grow close to the water's edge, but are high pruned so that crowding is not too excessive.

This whole feature, consisting of two fairly isolated ponds with varied shoreline and profile, plus scattered small islands and some shallow pools nearby, is situated in a wetland of moderate diversity, and provides additional, more varied niches. A fence surrounds the ponds to exclude grazing animals.

The main interest here is duck flighting, but the site serves as an important year-round habitat for nesting duck and waders, as well as being a locally important habitat for frogs and toads.

Table 3.5 Habitat assessment profile – Site 1, Borders Farm

Land holding BORDERS FARM   Habitat type WETLAND   Habitat number 1   Date 8/3/91

A *Physical features*

1 Land use   Past uses ROUGH GRAZING   Present uses WILDLIFE HABITAT ONLY

2 Physical conditions

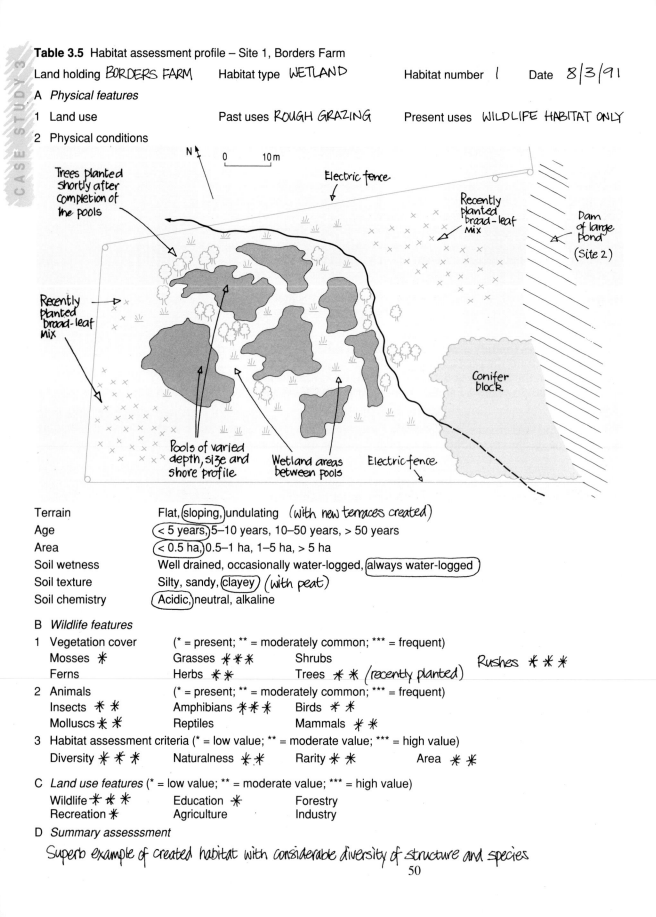

Terrain	Flat, (sloping,) undulating *(with new terraces created)*
Age	(< 5 years,) 5–10 years, 10–50 years, > 50 years
Area	(< 0.5 ha,) 0.5–1 ha, 1–5 ha, > 5 ha
Soil wetness	Well drained, occasionally water-logged, (always water-logged)
Soil texture	Silty, sandy, (clayey) *(with peat)*
Soil chemistry	(Acidic,) neutral, alkaline

B *Wildlife features*

1 Vegetation cover   (* = present; ** = moderately common; *** = frequent)

    Mosses *   Grasses ***   Shrubs   Rushes ***

    Ferns   Herbs **   Trees ** *(recently planted)*

2 Animals   (* = present; ** = moderately common; *** = frequent)

    Insects **   Amphibians ***   Birds **

    Molluscs **   Reptiles   Mammals **

3 Habitat assessment criteria (* = low value; ** = moderate value; *** = high value)

    Diversity ***   Naturalness **   Rarity **   Area **

C *Land use features* (* = low value; ** = moderate value; *** = high value)

    Wildlife ***   Education *   Forestry

    Recreation *   Agriculture   Industry

D *Summary assesssment*

Superb example of created habitat with considerable diversity of structure and species

Small groups of alder and willow occur around the ponds and, since fencing off, there has been some quite considerable rowan regeneration. On the south-west side of the fenced area, a variety of other broad-leaved trees have been planted to 'frame' the feature.

Three hides were erected on completion of the ponds. The area of rough-grazed wetland adjacent to the fenced area gives added diversity.

A habitat assessment checklist using the criteria shown in Table 3.4 is given for all three sites in Table 3.6.

Table 3.6 Habitat assessment for Sites 1, 2 and 3

Criterion	Rating		
	Site 1	*Site 2*	*Site 3*
A	**Open water**		
1 Naturalness	****	****	****
2 Diversity			
2.1 Plants	**	**	**
2.2 Invertebrates	***	**	**
2.3 Structural	***	****	***
3 Rarity	**	**	**
B	**Wetlands**		
1 Naturalness			
1.1 Water quality	****		****
1.2 Drainage	****		****
2 Diversity	***		***
3 Rarity	**		**
4 Area	**		*

The River Ouse, Buckingham

Wildlife assessment took three forms: an original river corridor survey, reference to existing survey data and consultation with relevant conservation organisations and local experts. The basis for the assessment was the river corridor survey undertaken in Summer 1987 at the outset of the design process. A survey summary is given in Box 3.1 and a section of the river corridor map is shown in Figure 3.7 (both overleaf). The methodology employed was basically that recommended by the Nature Conservancy Council in its draft guidelines, and involved a single experienced surveyor walking along the edge of the river, mapping the main habitats and dominant plant species. Although concentrating on the channel, margins and banks, adjacent land use was also recorded.

In addition to the river corridor survey, a limited bird survey was undertaken in 1988, and use was made of data relating to fish populations, to invertebrate numbers and diversity, and to water quality monitoring data

Box 3.1 Summary of river corridor survey

Adjacent land use At Bourton Mill, the adjacent land is mainly amenity grassland; from the farm access bridge downstream to the confluence there is some arable cultivation followed by semi-improved pasture on the left bank, with improved and semi-improved pasture on the right bank.

Banks The banks are generally fairly steep, up to 2 metres, the effects of erosion occasionally forming vertical earth banks; shelves have been formed where the banks have slumped. Much of the bank is subjected to grazing pressure, and **poaching** has created some shallow margins. The vegetation consists of ruderals, herbs and grasses, including comfrey, meadowsweet, gypsywort and marsh woundwort. Apart from some mature willows at Bourton Mill and below the farm access bridge, trees and shrubs occur only occasionally along the left bank, and are absent from most of the right bank.

Margins There are fringes of emergent vegetation along much of the length; species include branched bur-reed, greater pond sedge and great reedmace. The shallow margins and shelves support a variety of marginal plants including water-cress, water forget-me-not, water chickweed and water speedwell.

Channel The channel has a varied structure of gravel riffles, shoals and pools. The gravel riffles have an associated flora, notably river water-dropwort, stream water-crowfoot and horned pondweed, whilst the slack areas include yellow water-lily, shining pondweed, arrowhead and bulrush. In addition to the fishery interest, these habitats support numerous swans and waterfowl, including little grebe.

from routine sample points in the area. Consultation with local organisations produced other data, as well as informed comment, with the Royal Society for the Protection of Birds providing data from surveys along this section of river that it undertook in 1983.

The combination of these surveys shows that, despite the managed nature of the watercourse and adjacent land, it provides a relatively good wildlife habitat. The physical structure of the channel was diverse, with good riffle–pool sequences, especially in the lower sections downstream. The presence of large stands of river water-dropwort, stream water-crowfoot and horned pondweed was particularly valuable in the gravel riffles, and these can be expected to be rich in invertebrate diversity and density. Deeper slack-water was also present, just upstream of Maids Moreton weir, and this supported breeding pairs of tufted duck and little grebe.

Despite the relatively high banks, there were large and extensive fringes of emergent plants, such as great reedmace and greater pond sedge, with assemblages of marginal plants where slumping or cattle poaching had produced water-level shelves. Trees were largely absent from the riverside, except locally near Bourton Mill and the ring-road bridge. The absence of wood or scrub adjacent to the river was reflected in the low numbers of birds such as sedge warblers and whitethroats recorded in the Royal Society for the Protection of Birds survey. Similarly, the absence of low banks or adjacent marshy fields was reflected in the absence of waders, such as redshank and snipe.

The upper section of river through the Bourton Mill site was generally poorer in habitat value than the downstream sections. This may reflect increased disturbance from people, or the impact of urban run-off and the more managed nature of the watercourse within the urban fringe, as well as its past management. For instance, large, well-developed meander loops only occurred downstream of the ring-road. The variations in depth and flow pattern associated with the meanders were particularly valuable for wildlife, creating a diversity of habitats both within the channel and on the margins.

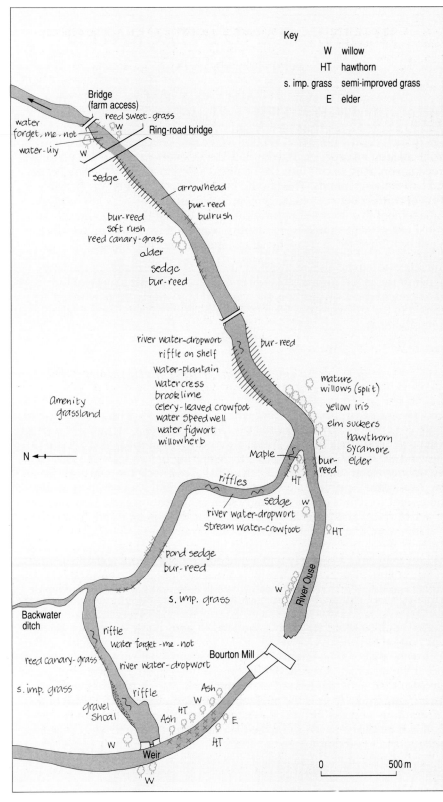

Key

W	willow
HT	hawthorn
s. imp. grass	semi-improved grass
E	elder

Bridge
(farm access)

reed sweet-grass
W
Ring-road bridge

water
forget-me-not
water-lily
W

sedge

arrowhead
bur-reed
bulrush

bur-reed
soft rush
reed canary-grass
alder
sedge
bur-reed

river water-dropwort
riffle on shelf
water-plantain
watercress
brooklime
celery-leaved crowfoot
water speedwell
water figwort
willowherb

bur-reed

mature
willows (split)

yellow iris

elm suckers
hawthorn
sycamore
elder

amenity
grassland

Maple
bur-reed

N

riffles
HT

sedge W

river water-dropwort
stream water-crowfoot

HT

pond sedge
bur-reed

W

River Ouse

s. imp. grass

Backwater
ditch

riffle
water forget-me-not

reed canary-grass

river water-dropwort

Bourton Mill

s. imp. grass

riffle

gravel
shoal

Ash
W
HT
Ash

Ash
E

W

HT

Weir

W

0   500 m

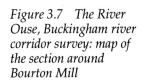

Figure 3.7   The River
Ouse, Buckingham river
corridor survey: map of
the section around
Bourton Mill

53

Chapter 4

BUSINESS AND INTEGRATED ASSESSMENT

The earlier stages of assessment should have clarified the value of your water or wetland site as a landscape feature and as a habitat for wildlife. This chapter focuses on the next stage, which is business assessment (used here to include any non-conservation usage and not necessarily implying a profit-making enterprise). To complete the assessment part of the planning process, you need to combine the business assessment with the landscape and habitat assessments. This should enable you to identify any possible areas of conflict between management in pursuit of business interests and management to enhance conservation value. One of the main aims of integrated assessment should be to identify ways in which any such conflicts might be minimised and any beneficial interactions maximised.

Consideration must also be given to the attitudes and values of the landowner or manager, as this will clearly influence the formulation of the management plan. In addition, the views of any other people who have an interest in the site may provide a new perspective to be taken into account in the assessment.

4.1 The uses of water and wetlands: business assessment

There is a great variety of possible uses to which open water and, to a lesser extent, wetlands may be put. Water is a resource that can be used to fulfil many needs: the irrigation of crops, the watering of livestock, the provision of drinking water, the rearing of fish and as a coolant in industry. Major rivers and canals provide a transport system, and all watercourses, water bodies and wetlands are increasingly seen as recreation sites. This may be for active water and game sports and also for the quieter pursuits of simply walking, watching and enjoying the water. Watercourses also serve the function of disposal routes for waste products. Some of these uses, especially the last, may have a severely damaging effect, both on the water itself and on the habitat. However, with care and forethought, the environmental impact can be greatly reduced, and in some cases making use of the water may even enhance its value for wildlife.

As well as the use of the water or wetland in your defined area of interest, it is important to consider the usage of the surrounding area, particularly the catchment area of any stream or river. This is obviously of particular importance if the watercourse is altered in some way by upstream users so that the effects of their activities are felt at downstream sites. A polluting effluent discharging into a river is the most obvious example of this. The use of the surrounding land can influence a watercourse or wetland either adversely, as shown by the effects of drainage or spray drift, or beneficially, if the land use favours conservation.

Using water for domestic water supply, agriculture and industry

Water is abstracted from rivers, reservoirs, lakes and groundwater for the purpose of supplying the public with **potable water**, for direct use by industry, for electricity generation and for agriculture. Three-quarters of this water comes from surface sites, the rest from groundwater sources.

In England and Wales, the volume of water abstracted at any particular point is controlled by licence to ensure a continuous water supply for the consumer and, it is hoped, to guarantee that the source is not over-used. In most parts of the country this can be achieved, although extended periods of dry weather can create difficulties, as we all know. The demand for water is increasing and, as described in Chapter 3, in some areas over-abstraction has already caused permanent lowering of the water level in rivers or even led to them drying out completely. If abstraction is properly controlled, this should never happen, but unfortunately demand has simply exceeded supply in some areas and the needs of consumers have had to be put before environmental considerations.

The effects of abstraction on any particular stretch of river are most likely to be visible in summer at times of lower flow. Smaller streams, especially those with variable flow, are more vulnerable to the ill-effects of abstraction. As well as a reduction in water volume, these effects may include a reduction in spring activity and a general lowering of the water table. Because of the reduced water volume, higher water temperatures are likely in hot weather and there will be less water to dilute any incoming effluent, both of which will adversely effect water quality. Bankside vegetation will also suffer if the water level is lowered or its normal fluctuations are disturbed.

In comparison with the volumes required for water supply and industry, agricultural usage is relatively small and requirements are often obtained from local sources. However, because there are a large number of abstraction points, and these are more likely to be on small streams and to be less well controlled, the potential effect may be important locally. Agricultural uses include irrigation, watering livestock and washing down yards.

The beneficial side of fulfilling water supply requirements has been the creation of numerous ponds, lakes and reservoirs of all sizes. Construction of **impoundments** and reservoirs is preferable to direct abstraction from rivers, in so far as it allows storage of water from periods of higher flow, thus reducing the possible damage caused by high demand in summer. This is not to deny, though, that the environmental impact of new reservoirs can be devastating. However, as well as their primary function of water supply, many of these water bodies provide valuable habitats for wildlife.

All ponds, streams and rivers that are also used by farm livestock for drinking can suffer severe localised damage at the water's edge as the ground is poached by their trampling hooves. This creates extremely muddy water, may cause progressive collapse of the banks and can also cause a localised but severe pollution problem from excreta. Having said that, wading birds may enjoy the wet, muddy conditions along poached river edges.

Using watercourses as drains

The importance of drainage to agriculture has been recognised for centuries, as providing improved conditions for plant growth, reduced crop damage caused by flooding and improved **trafficability** of the soil. These benefits have allowed land that was previously unsuitable for agriculture to be

Land drainage

brought into use, and encouraged intensification in existing fields. Better drainage has also allowed a change of use to more profitable enterprises, and reduced production costs by improving access to the land and extending the grazing season.

In the recent past, the necessity for draining has been distorted by the policy of grant-aiding, which has led some farmers to consider draining land that previously would have remained unaltered. Thus wetland sites have been totally destroyed for the sake of a short-term gain in improved agricultural land, but little or no long-term advantage, given that the silting up of drains necessitates yet further work. Grant aid is no longer generally available, but on average about 70 000 hectares per annum are drained on a continuing basis, the majority of which probably involves uprating and rejuvenating old schemes. There are still approximately 30 000 hectares of new drains installed each year.

The methods of field drainage adopted depend on local soil conditions and the resources available at the time. Open ditches are effective in free-draining soils, otherwise unlined **mole drains** or **piped drains,** spaced to suit the expected rainfall and hydraulic characteristics of the soil, are used.

Open-ditch draining of upland blanket bogs is known as **hill gripping** or moorland gripping. This is used to improve pasture for sheep or to increase numbers of red grouse, although several studies have strongly suggested that very little pasture improvement is achieved. Because of the poor water permeability of peat bogs, the effects of drainage are limited to within 1 or 2 metres of the ditch, where there can be some increase in heather at the expense of bog mosses, cotton-grass and liverworts. The main effect of gripping is to increase the speed of surface water run-off, which increases the threat of flooding, can cause erosion along watercourses and siltation downstream. Modern techniques of moorland gripping introduce an extremely unnatural visual component into the landscape. Regularly spaced, dark scars cutting across hillsides can completely destroy the beauty of upland moors. When used prior to further 'improvement' or afforestation, the ultimate effect is even worse.

The 'knock-on' effects of drainage – lowering of the water table and of the water level in streams in the surrounding area – were described in Chapter 3. Another result of land drainage, which may not be foreseen, is the release of **ochre** into streams and rivers, causing the water to turn brown, which is at best unsightly and may also be damaging to some plants and animals. This is a problem that is restricted to areas with the appropriate soil type, but can be forecast if thorough surveying is undertaken.

If water from field drains is discharged into a stream or river, the receiving waters may be adversely affected, as they could be by any discharge. Water quality may deteriorate through changes to the flow regime of the river, greater turbidity and increased run-off from surrounding land. Drainage water may contain fertiliser or pesticide if these have recently been applied to a field. Good agricultural practice should reduce the loss of these chemicals, for example by applying the appropriate amounts and by avoiding application during wet weather, but none the less some will probably leach down into the soil drains.

Despite these various environmental disadvantages of land drainage, it should be noted that the ditches may, if properly managed, provide rich wildlife habitats because of the combination of water and marginal vegetation.

The river engineer's aim is to minimise the quantity of water that can flood surrounding land and to improve the capacity of a channel to remove excess water. To achieve this, bends are straightened, channels are dredged and lined, riffles, islands, overhanging trees, other vegetation and any other possible obstacle are removed. From the hydraulic engineer's point of view, the most efficient channel has a trapezoid cross-section (see Figure 4.1), but this takes no account of the needs of wildlife. The destruction of natural river form by channelisation increased in the 1960s and 1970s. Fortunately, more enlightened methods are usually now employed, and the necessary flood protection can still be achieved without such great environmental cost (see Chapter 5).

Flood protection

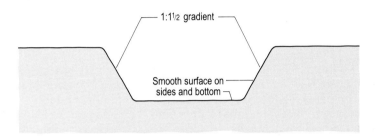

1:1½ gradient

Smooth surface on sides and bottom

Figure 4.1 Trapezoid river channel to maximise water flow

Removal of wastewater

Rivers and streams receive wastewater from a great many sources: sewage effluents, industrial discharges, agricultural wastewaters, run-off from roads and all other surfaces. The river water provides a unique service in diluting, dispersing and removing the wastewater and its polluting load. If effluents are properly treated before discharge, little damage is done. Problems arise where treatment is inadequate or non-existent. Domestic sewage is almost always treated to some extent before discharge to inland waters. Usually treatment consists of primary settlement to remove solids, biological treatment to remove organic matter, a second settlement stage and possibly further final treatment before discharge. Many sewage treatment works were designed and built many decades ago, and difficulties have arisen as populations have increased and the works have had to cope with volumes of sewage beyond their design capacity. Effluent quality is unlikely to reach the required standard when the works are overloaded in this way.

Many industrial effluents are discharged into the sewers, and water service companies levy charges on industry, depending on the strength and volume of the effluents. The nature of these wastes is extremely varied, and some are more easily treated than others. Given sufficient dilution, many trade effluents are satisfactorily treated by the bacteria responsible for the biological treatment of domestic sewage. Great care must be taken to ensure that toxic wastes do not enter the sewage treatment works, as these may kill the bacteria doing all the good work. This is even more important if discharge is direct to a watercourse, where the damage would be to a much wider environment.

River quality in England and Wales is the responsibility of the National Rivers Authority, which monitors all major discharges from municipal and industrial sources. Small and irregular discharges to streams are unlikely to be so well monitored, and these are frequently the cause of major pollution incidents. Pollution from farm waste has increased over the last decade, correlating with changes in agricultural practice. Intensive livestock production creates large volumes of slurry, which requires efficient storage and possibly treatment and disposal if on-farm usage cannot deal with it. Silage liquor seeping from inadequate silage clamps is even more polluting than slurry if it enters watercourses. The third major source of pollution by farm waste is yard washings, which should be kept separate from other surface water drainage, and not be discharged to ditches or streams.

Statistics of reported pollution incidents are likely to underestimate the pollution derived from **non-point sources**, such as run-off from fields. This is very difficult to spot, as drainage water seeps into streams all along field boundaries.

Using water for transport and recreation

Recreational use of water varies from active sports, such as water-skiing and wind-surfing, to the simple pleasures of walking and watching and listening to water and wildlife. The commercial potential of these different pursuits varies widely, as does their environmental impact, both on the water and on the surrounding area. People are attracted by water and the variety of possible leisure activities associated with it, and they will require land-based facilities, such as car parks, toilets, picnic areas and good footpaths. All these need careful planning, design and construction in order to minimise their environmental impact and to ensure that some areas are allowed to remain undisturbed for wildlife. Information and interpretation centres and organised nature trails can guide people to areas where some disturbance is acceptable, and, it is hoped, keep them away from quieter areas.

Motorised boats

Motorised boats are inevitably confined to larger rivers, canals and lakes where the depth and width of water are sufficient. Apart from a few ferries and some commercial transport, the majority of motorised boats are for leisure use. Cruisers and narrowboats have become increasingly popular over recent years, putting pressure on the limited capacity of the inland waterways system.

The major problems for the aquatic environment are bank erosion from the wash of boats and pollution by boats and their users. Canals, although artificial, were built to accommodate slow-moving, horse-drawn barges, and the banks were not designed to withstand the erosive power of the waves created by motorised boats. Speed limits, if adhered to, can reduce the amount of wash, as can certain designs of boat hull. Pollution from boats has been reduced, as most are now fitted with chemical toilets that can be emptied at special disposal points, rather than discharging wastes directly into the water.

Non-powered boats

Leisure use by non-powered boats poses fewer environmental problems, simply because they are slower and quieter. Sailing boats and dinghies are confined to larger bodies of water and rivers; rowing boats and punts are popular on mature rivers, particularly in or near provincial towns. Canoes can be used on many lakes and watercourses, although the more interesting waters for the canoeist are found in boulder-strewn hill streams and rivers.

There is relatively little threat to wildlife resulting from the use of non-powered boats, except as a result of disturbance in normally secluded areas, to which breeding birds are particularly vulnerable.

Other watersports

Wind-surfing and water-skiing have become extremely popular in recent years. They are, of course, confined to lakes where sufficient space is available, such as reservoirs and flooded gravel pits. These sites are also in demand for other sporting activities, such as angling, as well as for wildlife. These different requirements tend to be incompatible, because of the noise and disturbance from skiers and surfers.

One solution to this problem is to create and mark zones within a lake that are reserved for each of the different uses (see Chapter 5). This can go some way towards reducing the disturbance, but is not so successful against noise or the effects of wash and churning by water-ski boats, which spread over the whole lake regardless of marker buoys.

Angling is the most popular participation sport in Britain. Approximately four million people fish on rivers, canals, ponds and lakes of all sizes and types, mostly for coarse fish.

Angling

The main growth area commercially is in stillwater trout fisheries, situated in either existing or purpose-built lakes and ponds. In still water, trout need a depth of approximately 3 metres and the pond should be quite large, at least 0.4 hectare. The introduced rainbow trout do better than the native brown trout in still water, because they are more tolerant of warmer water with a lower dissolved oxygen level and they grow faster. However, they have a shorter life span and are less hardy. Any game fishery must be restocked each year with fry, and coarse fish must be removed from the pond as they compete with the trout.

Coarse fish are less demanding; carp can flourish in warm, shallow ponds with an average depth of about 1.2 metres. Many old, unmanaged ponds contain large numbers of small fish, particularly roach and rudd. Before establishing a coarse fishery, old ponds should be drained and cleared of existing fish stocks, but recurring costs are less than for game fishing, as annual restocking is not necessary.

Artificial stocking with fish must always be carried out in consultation with the local Fisheries Officer of the National Rivers Authority, who can advise on choice of species and stocking rates.

Generally, anglers prefer an attractive natural environment, so efforts spent on improving the environment may well bring commercial advantage as well as benefiting wildlife. There is usually room for compromise when the interests of anglers and conservation do not coincide. Bankside vegetation needs management for fly fishing, as tall bushes and trees interfere with casting a line. Rather than cutting back all vegetation, 'swims' or fishing stations with wooden platforms can be created, spaced along the bank, or alternatively pontoons can be built out into the water. Clearly marking appropriate positions for anglers and the paths by which to reach them will also reduce the likelihood of general trampling of bankside plants.

Predation by heron can be an expensive problem, particularly in game fisheries. Heron are deterred by steep banks, but this is not good for wildlife. A compromise with some steep and some shallow slopes and an acceptance of some losses due to natural predation may be the best approach.

The compatibility of fisheries with uses other than angling and with the interests of wildlife depends largely on the intensity of fishing. A low intensity obviously creates less disturbance, but also reduces profit. Frequent and heavy use of a fishery will increase profitability, but is bound to increase environmental impact. Many of the problems created by such an enterprise are caused by the anglers themselves. The thoughtless angler will trample plants, leave litter and be careless about collecting hooks and line. Until they were banned in 1987, discarded lead weights were a major hazard. Swans are particularly vulnerable to lead poisoning, as they pick up the lead shot with gravel from the river or lake bed. This is then held in the gizzard and used to grind up the plant material that forms the major part of their diet. Since the ban, Britain's swan population has recovered remarkably quickly and now stands at the highest it has been for 40 years.

Income from fishing can be derived in a number of ways. Angling clubs will pay farmers rent for the exclusive use of ponds or stretches of river. Alternatively, the farmer may sell day-tickets to individuals, or offer fishing as part of the attraction for farm holiday accommodation.

Shooting

Despite the apparent conflict between shooting wild birds and conservation, managing ponds and lakes to encourage water birds for sport generally enhances the environment for other animals and plants as well. Ducks and geese need seclusion, aquatic invertebrates and plants for feeding and bankside vegetation for protection and nest sites. All of these contribute to a balanced, diverse habitat from which all species may benefit. Any disturbance from shooting is limited to the season from September to January, and a pond should only be shot over at a minimum interval of three weeks.

Conflicts can occur with other sports, such as angling, as some coarse fish, particularly bream and perch, feed on the midge larvae that are an important component of the diet of ducklings. These fish species are therefore best kept at low population levels if waterfowl production is the main aim.

To encourage ducks into flight ponds at dusk, additional feed is supplied by broadcasting wheat or barley into shallow water. The quantity of food supplied must be carefully monitored, as too much can be damaging to the pond as well as making the waterfowl too fat and contented, thereby reducing their 'sport' value.

Spent lead shot is another important source of lead in the aquatic environment. Considerable amounts of lead pellets fall into the water or onto the surrounding land. From the waterfowl's point of view, lead pellets on the bottom of a pond are generally more harmful than those on the bank, as the former are more likely to be eaten, so shooting positions and hides should be located so that most of the spent shot falls on land rather than in the water.

Using water and wetlands for other commercial enterprises

Fish farming

Trout farming has increased very rapidly since the mid-1970s and is predominantly carried out on chalk-fed rivers in lowland areas. Trout farms require large quantities (up to 160 megalitres per day) of very clean water, so they have been established on high-quality rivers where water is abstracted into the farm tanks and returned downstream. The fish are kept at a high density in tanks, and the returned water contains unconsumed food and faecal waste, which pollutes the river with organic matter, solids and ammonia and reduces dissolved oxygen. Because of the large volumes involved, the wastes are extremely dilute when discharged to the river, but they still have a deleterious effect, as they constitute such a large proportion of the total river volume.

Crops

There are several possibilities for crops grown in or on water or wetlands, although these are mostly on a small scale with a relatively limited market.

However, they may provide opportunities for farm diversification if the growing conditions are suitable and the marketing potential is investigated.

There are many different species and varieties of willow, all of which grow well near water and several of which have some commercial potential.

Willow trees have been pollarded for centuries. Traditionally, this was done for firewood and also to produce rods for fence rails and posts. In addition nowadays, willows have a use in the manufacture of corrugated sections of cardboard boxes, which require a hardwood pulp with short fibre length, which willow can provide. Other commercial possibilities include cricket-bat willows and using willows for fuel. Trials with a vigorous Baltic species have suggested that stands of regularly coppiced willow can be used to provide timber for wood-burning stoves, or be compressed into fuel briquettes.

Osiers are another traditional crop from wetlands. Grown in **withy beds**, usually adjacent to rivers, they were cut to ground level every winter to produce slender rods for basket-making. This traditional industry is now a rare craft skill, but basketware is popular, and the market for it at present is almost entirely supplied by imported baskets which could possibly be supplanted by home-grown produce. Annual cutting of withy beds means they are of little value for wildlife. Rotational cutting, say over four years, creates a much richer environment for wildlife, although the commercial value of the osiers may be reduced.

Reed continues to be required for thatching, and management of reed beds for this purpose can be compatible with the needs of wildlife. Thatchers prefer one-year-old reed, but annual cutting of an entire bed would destroy the continuity of habitat and also weaken the reed. If the bed is cut in sections on a two-year rotation, so that each year some part remains undisturbed, this provides a continuing home for the warblers, tits and perhaps bitterns that live there.

4.2   Business assessment methods

The methods used for business assessment do not differ greatly from those described earlier for landscape and habitat assessment. The main components are:

▷   observation of the site, including use of sketch maps, drawings, diagrams, photographs, etc. where appropriate;

▷   data from other sources, e.g. the National Rivers Authority, local authorities, fishery records, etc., particularly as some uses of a site are not always within direct control of the landowner.

For the purposes of assessment, you should make note of any abstraction from the river or stream, including any upstream of your site. If possible, find out how much water is abstracted and when, if the demand is seasonal, as it would be for irrigation. Licences for abstraction from main rivers are required in England and Wales from the National Rivers Authority as designated by the Water Act 1989. The Authority should have information on licences granted for abstractions affecting your river or stream.

Abstraction

The presence of land drains affecting your site may not be immediately apparent. Local knowledge of the history of the area may be useful. In some cases, pipes can be seen protruding from river banks, but often the only sign will be a small ditch occasionally containing some water. Note the use of the land that is drained and whether it has agricultural chemicals applied to it. In existing wetland areas, it is obviously unlikely that these are drained at present. However, if you are considering restoring a wetland, the presence, location and type of land drain will be important. Similarly, historical information from maps and other documents on the former courses of streams and sites of wet ditches can be relevant. Further information may also be available from the Agricultural Development and Advisory Service.

Wastewater

Simple observation will provide considerable information on the use of a watercourse for wastes. Floating debris, scum and the ubiquitous supermarket trolley are all obvious signs. Heavy deposits of silt or mud on the bottom, or stirred up in the water, will also be easily seen. In many cases, however, the effects will only be reflected by the plant and animal populations, as described in Chapter 3.

Pipes visibly disgorging their contents cannot be mistaken. It may be possible to work out where the wastewater is coming from, and whether it is likely to be a threat. Discharge pipes from sewage treatment works or industrial sites should be noted. Rainwater running off from roads is usually discharged directly to streams or ditches, and can carry a highly polluting cocktail of organic matter, lead, zinc and hydrocarbons. Do not forget that your assessment of water usage should include the whole catchment area, particularly any discharge points upstream of your site of interest, as these will have a direct influence on the downstream water quality.

Transport and recreation

Simple observation will again yield the best information on the use of the water by people boating, angling or pursuing other sports. Make note of the type of activity and its impact on the environment. Have banks been eroded or trampled? Can access arrangements be improved? Are there problems caused by the number of people using the site, such as litter, car parking, etc?

Additional information on a fishery may be obtained from the fishery manager. This could include the type and quantity of fish stocked, how the site was prepared prior to stocking, the number of anglers using the site and the size of the annual catch. Anglers themselves may also provide anecdotal information, although their traditional tendency to exaggerate should, perhaps, be taken into account.

4.3   Integrating conservation and business assessments

The final stage of the site assessment is the integration of the landscape, habitat and business assessments. The information that you have collected should enable you to identify the conflicts and beneficial interactions between conservation and other uses. This can then be used to help you to decide on your objectives, that is, what you want to achieve in managing the site. It will also enable you to identify the constraints, and the degree to which these are within your control.

In the last few years, many water and wetland sites have been maintained or created solely for conservation purposes. As people have become more aware of the threats to these important habitats, many caring landowners and managers have been prepared to invest effort and money simply for the benefit of the environment. This attitude simplifies the planning process, because there is no conflict of purpose if the objective is solely to encourage wildlife. However, even when conservation is the primary or only aim, there are still constraints to be considered. Some of these will be beyond your control and may severely restrict your options, such as unsuitable geology, inadequate water supply or pollution from adjacent properties. These constraints may combine to prevent the first objective of creating a good habitat for all forms of wildlife. You may have to consider modifying your plans to accommodate these constraints. For example, if your pond is not able to support fish, you may have to limit your intentions to providing an inviting habitat for invertebrates and amphibians.

In circumstances in which business interests must also be considered, further constraints on management for conservation are likely to emerge, and should be identified through the assessment process.

If the conservation and business aspects of wet areas are considered in isolation, they tend to become increasingly incompatible. On the other hand, if they are closely integrated, many beneficial interactions can be developed. For example, farm ponds stocked with trout for angling can still provide immense opportunities for other wildlife to thrive, if properly constructed and maintained. Similarly, large reservoirs can be used for water sports and, if properly zoned, there will be ample space for wildlife, particularly water-fowl, to feed or breed. In addition, if screening shelterbelts of trees are used, the watersports will not detract too much from the landscape value of the site. Of course, some uses – water abstraction, drainage and wastewater disposal – provide little benefit. Indeed, they are nearly always a constraint on other activities.

Finally, it must be remembered that integrated assessment should be used to view the water and wetland areas in the context of the land holding as a whole. This includes consideration of the rest of the catchment area and the links between the water bodies, watercourses and wetlands. It should also take into account the influence of surrounding land use on the water and wetlands.

4.4   Making your own integrated assessment

Make an integrated assessment of the water and wetland area(s) in your holding or study area, following the case study examples in the next section. Your assessment should include:

▷ a business assessment summary, listing the uses of the water or wetland area(s) (see Section 4.2);

▷ where appropriate, a map showing the relationship of the water or wetland area(s) to other land uses;

▷ a consideration of the conflicts between business usage and conservation, and any beneficial interactions;

▷ an indication of the land manager's objectives and relevant constraints.

4.5 Integrated assessment of the case study areas

Borders Farm

The policy on the farm has always been that the features were essentially being created for their own sake, and for the landscape, amenity and wildlife benefit of the farm and those who spend their time on and around it. Any financial gain from these features was an added bonus.

Fishing

A number of the ponds are stocked with trout from a local, accredited source. Mossbrae Lochan is stocked annually with around 100 brown trout and 50 rainbow trout. The number varies annually, depending on the information contained in the returns completed by visiting anglers.

Currently, two days of fishing per week are let in the season to two individuals, each of whom can bring one guest. Their catch is limited to six per day. The use of Mossbrae Lochan includes the use of the well-furnished fishing hut and a small rowing boat. The owner is obliged to provide the relevant safety equipment needed in the boat, such as life-jackets.

It is hoped that letting fishing of the ponds on the farm may be expanded to produce more revenue. This would necessarily mean the loss of the five remaining days of private use, or at least a part thereof, so that there would be 'costs' incurred in increasing the returns.

Predation of fish does occur. Heron and otter occasionally take a few fish, but these are tolerated and their presence enjoyed. Mink, on the other hand, are trapped when possible, as they are considered to do far more damage.

Game

The shoot on the farm, although small in scale, offers considerable variety: deer stalking and high-seats (chairs raised on a platform with ladder access to give a better view along the rides) in the forest; a good pheasant drive or rough shoot; and duck flighting.

The farm has three small flight ponds, and one of the larger ponds also provides good duck flighting. Site 3 is the most favoured site, with the two ponds attracting 30–40 duck in an evening, mostly mallard but occasionally some teal. These ponds are fed a bucket or so of barley twice a week during the season, or perhaps daily just prior to being shot. The ponds are shot by two or three guns only, around six times a season.

Currently, the shooting is very much a private interest and is not let. While it could be let, it is felt that the loss of privacy on the farm would be too high a price to pay, and also that the area of the farm is too small to accommodate a large, organised shoot. In addition, there would have to be more intensive keepering, which would be a further cost.

The pond and wetland features serve to diversify the landscape and habitat of the farm. Those people staying in the holiday cottages are encouraged to make the most of the farm for walking and birdwatching. These activities, plus fishing (on certain days) are offered in the advertisements for the cottages, and help to attract potential customers.

Finally, there is considered to be an added capital value to the farm as a consequence of the creation of the pond and wetland features, plus the work being done to enhance the structure of the woodlands.

Access

It is not likely that the farmer would choose to charge people for access to the area (even were he able to). Currently, although a minor road does run

64

through part of the farm, it is a dead-end track and is used by few people. Some walkers do come onto the farm and are allowed to walk through. There are no facilities for disabled people. The site has already been visited by organised groups as a training and demonstration feature, as well as a site of general interest. This has been permitted by goodwill and is not a money-making scheme.

The River Ouse, Buckingham

The prime reason or objective of the planned river works is to increase flood protection, both of the urban areas upstream and of the agricultural areas downstream of the main ring-road bridge near Bourton Mill.

Flood protection

Surface storm water from the housing estates north and south of the river at Bourton Mill drains into the river. It is necessary to ensure that at times of high river flow the drains are not submerged (drowned out), and that at peak flows the water does not back up the pipes such that it causes flooding of adjacent housing. Downstream of the ring-road, it is necessary to ensure that land drains installed in riverine fields continue to function effectively, and are not drowned out frequently. In many ways, the requirements of land drainage can thus be seen as a mirror of the requirements of flood protection, and the two are intrinsically linked.

Land drainage

Although this stretch of river contains no sources of industrial discharges, treated effluent from Buckingham Sewage Treatment Works enters the river in the downstream section below Maids Moreton weir. The quality of this discharge has been variable in the past, but recently extensive works have been undertaken to improve it. While producing a localised impact on water quality, the key requirement in relation to the proposed river works is that the quantity of water, or flow, must not be reduced at the point where the final effluent enters. In summer months, when river flows are naturally reduced, the amount of water passing the discharge point is critical in ensuring that the dilution of the final effluent is sufficient to meet the set legal and biological standards.

Discharges to the river

The farms in the downstream section of the river do not abstract water for irrigation purposes. However, the river is used for watering livestock, and at a number of locations there are cattle drinking bays. These provide the animals with access to water, and it is important that the water quality is maintained.

Agricultural use

At Bourton Mill, the owner retains historical rights to a flow through the mill structure, although the mill is no longer used and at the time of study was semi-derelict. Following discussion with the owner, it was agreed that the status quo regarding levels and flows through the mill should be maintained. There is therefore a requirement for a structure at the upstream end of the mill channel to allow 0.15 cubic metres per second to pass through the mill at low flow, and yet to restrict flows at times of flood to safeguard the mill building, which is in poor condition.

Recreation along the stretch takes two main forms: walking and fishing. Recognising the potential of the river, Buckingham Borough Development Company (BBDC) and Aylesbury Vale District Council (AVDC) proposed plans for a linear park to open up the river corridor through the town and out into the urban fringes along the Bourton Mill site. It was proposed that

Recreation

this should coincide with the river improvement works, and involve foot-path construction following the river channels, tree planting, closer management of grassland for recreation, removal and rationalisation of the overhead electricity wires, and the creation of new amenity ponds. Downstream of the ring-road bridge, the main recreation is fishing, with no formal public access. The main requirement for angling is a good habitat for fish, the only further requirement for anglers being appropriate access to the river.

Conservation

In addition to maintaining water quality, which would not be greatly affected by the works, the key components of the scheme were to maintain and enhance the physical diversity and structure of the river channel. Bankside shelves and margins were to be retained or recreated, as were pools and riffles in the channel itself. Prominent meander loops were to be totally retained, and the two existing weirs rebuilt, to maintain existing water levels and flow patterns. Tree planting and pond clearance would be undertaken where possible, and proposals for creation of a new backwater channel and three new ponds were put forward for the Bourton Mill site.

Conservation was also to include the archaeological and historical aspects of the site, as well as landscape considerations. Thus, it was decided early on that the weir at Bourton Mill would be rebuilt using natural stone. Similarly, it was decided to retain the old arched farm access bridge downstream of the ring-road, and to mitigate its restriction to the passage of floodwater by building a concrete **flume** beneath it.

The integration process

Integration of the various, and sometimes conflicting, requirements of the above factors in the scheme was achieved through detailed survey, consultation and scheme appraisal. A key requirement for the design engineers was that they should liaise not only with the BBDC, the AVDC and relevant landowners, but with the Anglian Water Recreation and Conservation Officer and, through him, with the various conservation and angling bodies. Thus the final design of the scheme and agreed methods of operation were achieved by joint consultation between engineering and environmental interests, with the conservation input having been an integral part of the process from the outset.

Initial work undertaken by Anglian Water Authority involved the river corridor survey, and analysis of existing information held by the Water Authority on the invertebrate, fishery and water quality interests for this stretch of river. The river corridor survey was carried out in Summer 1987, so that by the time initial project appraisal and design schemes had been formulated, this was already to hand. Regular discussions were also begun with the landscape architect's section of the BBDC, to ensure that co-ordination was achieved with its plans for the riverside walk and linear park.

In January 1988, details of the scheme were sent formally to the Nature Conservancy Council, the Countryside Commission, the Royal Society for the Protection of Birds, Berks, Bucks and Oxon Naturalists' Trust, Buckingham and District Angling Club, the Department of Biological Sciences at the University of Buckingham and the Buckingham County Archaeologist. In addition to details of the design brief, they were each supplied with a project appraisal document, a provisional programme of works and copies of the river corridor survey. Comments were requested on three main aspects:

▶ the value of the river corridor with respect to wildlife and archaeology;

- the design of the scheme in relation to important habitats and features;
- opportunities for enhancement of the river environment.

The responses and subsequent discussions with relevant persons were used to help modify the designs to take into account points raised.

In addition to the conservation survey of the river corridor, which was largely a botanical survey detailing habitat features relating to adjacent land use, river banks, margins and the channel itself, a survey on breeding birds was carried out in Summer 1988 to supplement records provided by the Royal Society for the Protection of Birds in correspondence. Neither the Nature Conservancy Council nor the local Naturalists' Trust identified any particularly important areas or habitat features, but the County Archaeologist raised the possibility of the discovery of artefacts. Although the proposals did not affect any known archaeological sites, it was thought that the works might uncover evidence of one of the two late Saxon burghs of Buckingham, which were believed to be in the vicinity. Monitoring by means of the intermittent presence of an archaeologist was therefore suggested.

Information on the various aspects of conservation was co-ordinated by the Recreation and Conservation Officer of Anglian Water. This was reviewed in conjunction with a detailed topographical survey of the river channel produced by the engineers. This key survey showed both the long section and typical cross-sections for the whole length of river being discussed. By examining the amount of material that needed to be removed from the channel at each cross-section in order to achieve the desired flood flow capacity, it was possible to describe the potential environmental impact of the works and propose mitigating measures and alternative designs or methods of working for each section.

The likely significant effects of the proposed scheme were summarised and are shown in Table 4.1 (overleaf).

Environmental impact appraisal

In addition to the potential impacts highlighted, it is important to recognise the two major impacts on the human environment that the scheme was intended to produce:

- improvement of surface water drainage to prevent flooding of adjacent urban areas caused by surcharging at periods of high river flow;

- improvements in channel capacity to prevent increased flooding of agricultural areas downstream, by balancing increased storm water discharge from the new housing developments.

Since neither Anglian Water Authority nor its successor own the river, integration of the conservation and engineering interests had also to include detailed discussion with the landowners of the riverine areas. In the upstream section this was readily achieved with the BBDC, as the Council's aims for the Bourton Mill area had already been included in early design proposals. Elsewhere this was not the case.

Although Anglian Water Authority had compulsory purchase powers to undertake essential flood protection works, landowner interests and cost considerations both constrained the width and choice of adjacent riverbank available for working. Furthermore, continuous tree cover could hinder access to the river for routine maintenance work.

Table 4.1 An environmental impact appraisal for river works on the River Ouse, Buckingham

Recreation	−	Temporary disruption to footpath users during scheme work
	+	Creation of new footpath system and improved access facilities
Landscape	+	New tree planting schemes to enhance river landscape
	+	New amenity ponds at Bourton Mill site
	+	Removal of existing storm water overflow pipe across Bourton Mill flood plain
	+	Creation of new cascade weir faced with natural stone at Bourton Mill to form an attractive waterside feature
	+	Long-term plans of BBDC to remove unsightly overhead electricity wires
Cultural heritage	+	Archaeological monitoring of excavation of new river channel bypassing Bourton Mill
	+	Retention of the arched farm access bridge downstream of the ring-road
Water	−	Temporary reduction in water quality for short distances due to dredging
	−	Permanent loss of 110 metres of existing bypass channel, which will be infilled
	+	Construction of 230 metres of additional backwater channel at Bourton Mill site
	+	Construction of a new 200 metre main channel bypassing Bourton Mill, complete with new weir
	+	Creation of three new amenity ponds on Bourton Mill site
	+	Clearance of two existing riverside ponds downstream of Maids Moreton
Flora	−	Damage to riverine habitat by dredging operation
	−	Loss of aquatic flora in channel to be backfilled
	+	Extensive new tree planting programme
	+	Creation and restoration of pond habitats and new river channels
Fauna	−	Temporary disturbance of birds, invertebrates and fish during dredging
	−	Permanent losses in channel to be backfilled
	+	Creation of new woodland habitats
	+	Creation and restoration of pond habitats and new river channels

Discussion with landowners produced agreement that all work would be done from the south side of the river. A variable amount of material would be taken out during dredging, the amount relating to that required to increase the food capacity of each particular cross-section to 17 cubic metres per second when bankfull. The exact profile of the final bank would be agreed on site once work began, but in all places at least one-third to one-half of the channel cross-section would not be touched by the dredging machine, thus leaving an undisturbed wildlife refuge.

Chapter 5

MAINTAINING AND IMPROVING EXISTING WATER AND WETLANDS

The first part of a full management planning exercise involves finding out 'where you are now' by making an integrated assessment of the water and wetlands on your holding, as described in Chapters 2, 3 and 4. This leads on to a consideration of 'where you would like to be' by exploring the strategic, management and tactical objectives for the area as a whole, as described in the foundation book and as illustrated briefly in the case studies at the end of Chapter 4. This chapter concerns the next part of the planning exercise: considering the range of options available to put your objectives into practice.

Appropriate management options fall into three categories:

1   *maintaining* a wet habitat in its present form because it is a valued landscape feature or because it has high wildlife quality or contains rare plants and/or animals;

2   *improving* a wet habitat of moderate or poor conservation value, by changing its visual appearance or by increasing the overall ecological diversity and/or encouraging particular wildlife species;

3   *creating* new wet habitats designed to blend in with the landscape and/or to support and encourage a wide diversity of wildlife and/or particular wildlife species.

This chapter concentrates on the first two categories, looking at conservation within existing wet habitats, whether these are small ponds or large rivers, and whether the objectives are to provide water, waste disposal, recreation, landscape value or wildlife habitat. In the next chapter, which looks at the creation of *new* wet habitats, particularly ponds and lakes, many of the considerations are the same as for existing wet habitats, but the ability to design for specific objectives is greater on a 'green field' site. As a consequence, some information of relevance to this chapter is included in the next chapter and vice versa.

Any one of the three options – maintaining, improving or creating – will inevitably lead to some physical disturbance of the habitat. It is important that this is kept to a minimum by the correct timing of any necessary work. In general, the winter months are the best time for any work involving dredging, clearance or similar upheaval, because at this time of year most aquatic life is dormant. Inevitably, many individual animals will still be lost, but by leaving some areas undisturbed the population should be able to rebuild in the spring. If the weather is very cold and there is ice to contend with, it may be better to do the work in late autumn or early spring rather than the depths of winter. The important thing is to avoid the growing season of spring and summer. In addition to this general rule, there may be local requirements to consider. The presence of over-wintering wildfowl may prevent work in mid-winter, and springtime working may be damaging to nesting birds or spawning amphibians. Surveying the site at different times of year should provide better information with which to judge the best time for remedial work.

There is also a fourth management option available – to do nothing at all. Stability of the environment is important, so do not think that action is necessarily required. Conservation may best be served by inactivity, at least at the present time. However, the cycle of management planning is continuous, and so you should regularly reassess the situation and possibly alter your maintenance plans to suit changed circumstances.

5.1 Managing water quantity

The mere presence of water means that wet habitats, particularly streams and rivers, are dynamic systems, constantly changing due to the processes of erosion and deposition. To maintain and improve them, a management programme is required that keeps the water in the right place and in the right quantities, both to ensure the continuation of the habitat and to fulfil any other needs that may apply. This may entail dredging, shaping channels and profiles, building embankments and abstaining from land drainage.

River engineering

The fundamental purpose of river engineering is to answer the needs for good drainage, flood control and adequate water supply. In some rivers, it will also be necessary to maintain deep channels for navigation and possibly to provide appropriate conditions for angling. The basic approach is to satisfy the needs of the engineer without causing permanent devastation of the habitat, by including conservation needs at the earliest stage of the engineer's plans. It is much easier and of greater value to retain all or part of a habitat than to try and recreate it after disruption.

Some of the techniques discussed here are only appropriate for organisations such as the National Rivers Authority to undertake, and are unlikely to be seriously considered by smaller concerns. However, the principles described apply at all levels, whether the object is a main river or a ditch. A ditch will not have quite the same potential for habitat diversity as a river, simply because it is smaller, but what potential there is can be realised by a sensitive approach to maintenance work, and drainage ditches can be very valuable wet habitats if managed appropriately.

Channel alteration may be considered necessary to prevent flooding and to improve drainage of surrounding land. At its simplest, this entails making a channel deeper so that it will be capable of containing more water, but there are many ways of achieving the same end, which will not damage the habitat and may in fact improve it. There are two general rules that should be followed :

▶   retain refuges for wildlife along the river to allow the plants and animals to recolonise the disturbed areas more quickly after the work is finished. This means working on small stretches at a time, returning in following years to work on the next sections, or planning to leave some areas untouched;

▶   it is most important wherever possible that work should only be carried out from one side of the river at a time. This ensures that the vegetation on the opposite bank is relatively undamaged and also limits the impact of heavy vehicles to one side only.

Flood banks   Flood banks built on either side of a channel leave the existing watercourse and its banks unaltered. Generally, least damage to wildlife occurs if flood banks are set back from the watercourse, and ideally the material to make them should be imported onto the site rather than dredged from the channel.

In a multi-stage channel, flood waters are contained within wide **berms** cut above normal water level, which increase the capacity of the immediate flood plain rather than the channel. The advantages to wildlife depend on minimising the disturbance to the channel. This can be done by constructing a berm on one side only or on alternate banks. In addition, with appropriate management, the berm itself may become a valuable wet grassland habitat (Figure 5.1).

Multi-stage channels

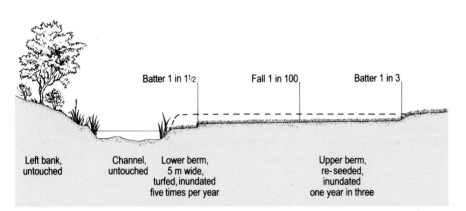
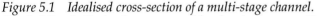

Figure 5.1   Idealised cross-section of a multi-stage channel.
*(Dashed line indicates former ground level, prior to excavation of flood berms. See Glossary for definition of **batter** as used here.) (Source: Lewis and Williams, 1984)*

A variant of the multi-stage channel is the shallow water berm designed to be submerged at all times. In gravelly streams, the berm is likely to remain bare of vegetation and could provide a feeding area for common sandpiper and other water birds. More often, the berm may be planted or colonised by emergent plants, thus providing shelter and food sources for many invertebrates and fish. There are many possible designs for a berm, depending on the site conditions. To encourage a range of aquatic plants, at least half of the berm should be submerged at times of lowest flow to a depth of approximately 20 centimetres. For effective bank protection, a berm 2 metres wide with a slope of 1 in 4 or less is recommended, and this can be planted with emergent plants. Even a very narrow berm or notch on an otherwise regular slope will generally improve the likelihood of successful colonisation by emergent plants.

If a channel has to be dredged and deepened, damage to the aquatic community can be reduced by dredging only two-thirds of the width or less. This allows the survival of the range of riverside communities from bank top to river bottom (Figure 5.2 overleaf). Care must be taken to excavate the correct width and depth of channel, as the effect on the water level is critical. If the channel is too deep, there is a danger that vegetation on the untouched bank will be left stranded above normal water level and die.

Partial dredging

Diversity of habitats within a river is as important as diversity at the water's edge and on the banks. Different communities of invertebrates, fish and

Conserving riffles and pools

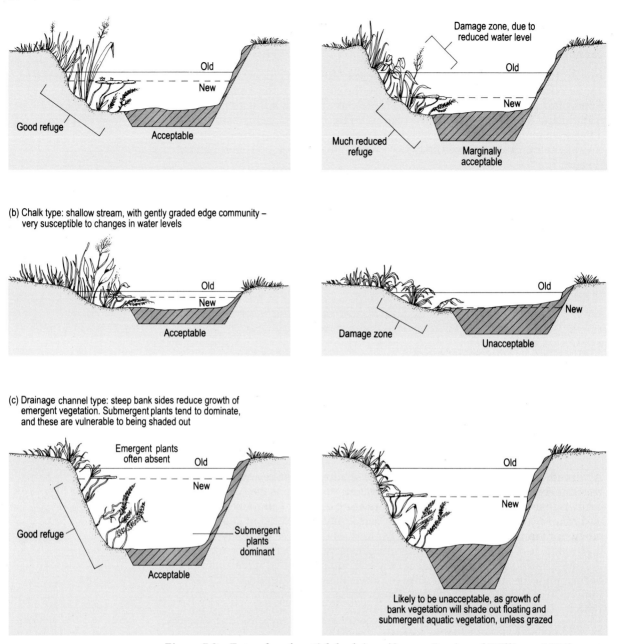

(a) Clay lowland type

Damage zone, due to
reduced water level

Old

New

Old

New

Good refuge

Much reduced
refuge

Acceptable

Marginally
acceptable

(b) Chalk type: shallow stream, with gently graded edge community –
very susceptible to changes in water levels

Old

New

Old

New

Acceptable

Damage zone

Unacceptable

(c) Drainage channel type: steep bank sides reduce growth of
emergent vegetation. Submergent plants tend to dominate,
and these are vulnerable to being shaded out

Emergent plants
often absent

Old

New

Old

New

Good refuge

Submergent
plants
dominant

Acceptable

Likely to be unacceptable, as growth of
bank vegetation will shade out floating and
submergent aquatic vegetation, unless grazed

Figure 5.2   Examples of partial dredging. (Source: Lewis and Williams, 1984)

excavated area

weed will live in the riffles, where the water is shallow and turbulent,
compared with deep pools. To conserve the diversity of habitats, the variations in depth of water and the nature of the substrate must also be conserved. When dredging is carried out, many of the riffles and pools will
inevitably be destroyed, but it is important to retain some sections of each of
the different underwater habitats to act as refuges. This requires careful
planning and mapping of the areas to be left undisturbed.

The existence of riffles and pools depends on many factors, including the volume of water, the type of substrate, the shape and form of the banks, obstructions, vegetation and others. To try to recreate lost riffles and pools is therefore extremely difficult and requires considerable expertise and experience. The hydraulic processes that created the variations in the first place will soon wash away artificial gravel deposits and fill in pools if they are in the 'wrong' place.

Meanders provide a range of opportunities for plants and animals. On the outside of a bend, the river steadily erodes the bank exposing a vertical cliff, if the sub-soil is of the appropriate consistency. Sand martins and kingfishers may find the cliff suitable for nest holes. The inside of the bend is an area of deposition of river silt and sand, providing shallow waters and a gently shelving bank, which is useful for ducks and easily colonised by plants.

Meander conservation

In the past, bypassing meanders to straighten a channel was standard practice used by drainage engineers, as it simplified the river profile. The abandoned meander was frequently used as a convenient hole in which to dump excavated spoil, and as a result the meander and the habitat diversity it provided were lost.

Figure 5.3 (overleaf) shows various ways of achieving the necessary channel improvement whilst maintaining the meander in one form or another.

The value of a low, stone weir built across a river channel is to increase channel diversity by creating pools of slightly deeper water and providing crevices and rocky surfaces in the weir itself. These also increase oxygenation of the water by breaking the flow over the weir, thus producing turbulence.

Weirs can be constructed very simply by laying blocks across a channel so that they are fully or partially submerged. The best material to use is natural stone if this is available. Alternatives are concrete bricks or stone-filled **gabion baskets**, although both of these have disadvantages. Concrete is unattractive and may alter the water chemistry as lime leaches out. Gabion baskets may be good alternatives in lowland rivers but should not be used in fast-flowing streams, as they will deteriorate and leave ugly, dangerous, rusty wire in the water.

Low stone weirs

The banks of rivers and streams (and also ponds and lakes) are particularly vulnerable parts of the aquatic environment. They are subject to potential erosion from all sides: from undercutting by the water beneath and from trampling by farm animals, people and machinery above. Added to this in some locations are the problems of boat wash and the resulting wave erosion to the banks. Collapsing banks destroy plant life, fill in a channel with sediment and muddy the water. Stabilising banks is therefore necessary, both to counteract possible damage and in response to the needs of the river or drainage engineer. The form of the river banks is closely linked to the form of the river channel. For wildlife conservation, the same underlying principle applies, that is, to try to retain the whole range of habitats and communities that existed before any work was undertaken – if not in their entirety then in part – so that recolonisation can take place as quickly as possible. A gentle, irregularly graded slope from land to water will allow a greater range of plant groups to become established than will a steep bank. It will also facilitate access for aquatic mammals and birds, particularly their young, and for land animals coming to the water to drink. Alternatively,

Bank form

Figure 5.3   Some options for meander conservation. (Source: Lewis and Williams, 1984)

(a) A flood bypass channel is cut across the meander, only taking flood flows. This option causes least disturbance to river habitats.

(a)

(b) A new channel is cut; at least 50 per cent of pre-scheme flows are maintained through the meander by a small, controlling weir on the main channel.

(b)

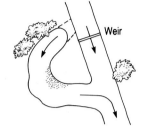

(c) A new channel is cut; flow and water levels in the meander are maintained by a small weir at the downstream end.

(c)

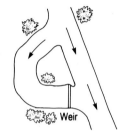

(d) A new channel is cut; the meander remains as a backwater, emptying and filling as a flood peak passes. A wetland, marshy habitat will gradually develop as the 'backwater' silts up.

(d)

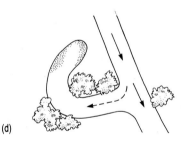

(e) A new channel is cut; the meander is cut off entirely and changes to a pond-type habitat.

(e)

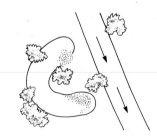
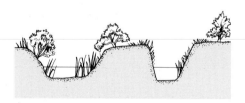

cliffs, if sandy or gravelly, are ideal for martins and kingfishers, while overhangs may attract fish seeking cover.

Essentially, bank protection involves building some kind of barrier between the water and the bank. Sheet piling and concrete are efficient but very ugly and clearly inhospitable to wildlife. Preferable alternatives include local stone, **faggoting**, gabions (illustrated in Figure 5.4), and fabric and mesh **revetment** products. Planting reeds and other robust species in association with these bank facings masks them from view, improves the protection provided and enhances the habitat.

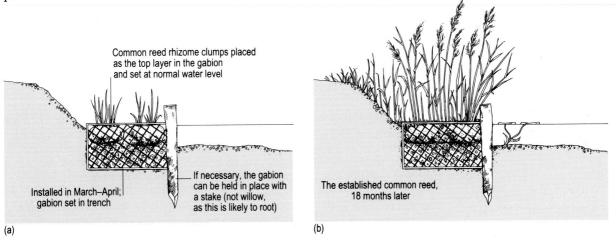

Figure 5.4 *Bank protection using rhizome clumps of common reed in stone-filled gabions. (Source: Lewis and Williams, 1984)*

Dredging ponds and ditches

There are fewer choices available for maintaining adequate depth of water in ponds and ditches. Periodic removal of the accumulating silt and debris is the only option. The methods for doing this depend on the size of the problem. Small ponds can be dug out by hand, although this is very tedious. Volunteer groups, such as the British Trust for Conservation Volunteers, may be willing to take this on. Pumping out may be possible, as long as the right sort of pump is used and providing that care is taken to dispose of the slurry. The best means of clearing out a pond or ditch is by mechanical excavator. For ponds up to 12 metres wide and for ditches, tracked or wheeled machines with buckets, rakes or cutters should be used. Larger ponds may need a dragline excavator.

During dredging operations, the potential of a pond for wildlife can be much improved by taking the opportunity to reprofile the edges of the pond to provide shelves in shallow water for plants (see Chapter 6). A pond should ideally be dug out to a depth of 2–3 metres. When excavating, great care must be taken not to damage the bottom sealing if there is one.

It is very important that some areas are left untouched by the excavation, so that plants and animals can survive through the clearance operation to colonise again once the work has finished. It is also important not to dredge too often. Some species, such as the ruddy darter dragonfly, take some time to recolonise after major disturbance to the habitat, and would never return to a site that was cleaned out too frequently.

75

There is one fundamental rule for maintaining wetlands, and that is not to drain them.

In some circumstances, marsh or wet grassland may be improved by creating pools of open water within the wetland area. This increases the diversity of habitats and may encourage plants and animals, particularly birds that previously were not present. Careful site assessment is essential to ensure that any change results in a net gain for conservation and not a loss. It should also be borne in mind that access for heavy machinery to excavate a pool may be difficult in wet soils. (Management of wet grasslands is covered in more detail in another book in the *Practical Conservation* series: *Grasslands, Heaths and Moors*.)

5.2   Managing water quality

An essential prerequisite for a healthy wet habitat is clean water. Controlling and, it is hoped, preventing pollution of the water is therefore of fundamental importance. If the source of pollution is within your control, pollution should be prevented at all costs. As well as improving the water quality of your wet habitat, this may also remove the possibility of prosecution. Difficulties arise if the source of pollution is outside your control, for example on adjacent land, or if the source is difficult to identify. In these circumstances, if friendly approaches to your neighbours are unsuccessful, you can enlist the help of the National Rivers Authority (in England and Wales) or the River Purification Board (in Scotland). It is possible to take legal action against polluters, although, as with all legal processes, this may take a long time and be expensive. It may be possible to protect a pond from pollution, either by creating an area of marsh at the inlet, which would intercept and clean inputs of polluted water, or by building a bund or embankment around the edges to deflect run-off to the outlet end of the pond.

Farm wastes

Agriculture has great potential for water pollution. Animal wastes, yard washings, silage liquor, pesticides, fertilisers and sheep dip can all cause severe pollution if allowed to reach fresh water, but this can be avoided by following correct handling and management procedures. Detailed discussion of such procedures is beyond the scope of this book, but the Agricultural Development and Advisory Service will advise on all aspects of farm waste management with water pollution prevention in mind, and the National Rivers Authority will provide an assessment of pollution risk.

The usual method of slurry disposal is land-spreading. Water pollution by rainwater run-off from this can be avoided by not spreading near a watercourse, on steeply sloping land or on dry, cracked, frozen or water-logged soil. Slurry application should be limited to not more than 50 cubic metres per hectare every three weeks. Dilute effluents must be applied at a rate slow enough to allow the liquid to percolate through the soil, not more than 5 millimetres per hour. The dangers from run-off can be reduced by using slurry injection machines, which introduce slurry directly into the soil beneath the surface.

Slurry application to arable land at a time of year or at a rate of application that will supply nutrients in excess of crop requirements can lead to excess nitrates in the soil, which may then leach into groundwater and thence to ponds and streams. For this reason, application to arable land is best done in spring rather than autumn or winter.

Adequate storage facilities are required for slurry and wastewater, and it is essential that these are designed, built and maintained to correct specifications. They must be big enough to accommodate the maximum volume produced by the livestock unit, including allowance for rainwater during short periods of heavy rain, as well as for normal rainfall. Leaking slurry stores cause pollution of groundwater, which may then seep through the soil into nearby streams and ponds. This can also result from rainwater percolating through piles of solid manures or silage clamps.

Separation of dirty waters, such as yard washings, from uncontaminated rainwater run-off not only reduces the volume of liquid requiring disposal, but also reduces the likelihood of heavy rain causing pollution from overflow of the drainage system. This means that, in a farmyard, separate drains are required for yard washings and for run-off from clean areas like roofs.

Dirty waters can be used as irrigation water, or disposed of by connection to the public sewer, or treated on the farm before discharge to surface waters. Consent to discharge would have to be obtained from the relevant authority. In England and Wales, this would be the water services companies for discharge to the sewers and the National Rivers Authority for discharge direct to surface waters.

It is essential to inspect ditches, streams and ponds regularly and frequently near any areas of storage, spreading or irrigation involving wastes, to look for any signs of pollution and to take immediate remedial action.

Pesticides

Pesticides may reach fresh water by accidental direct spraying or drift, by run-off and seepage into groundwater and by careless disposal of containers and unwanted chemicals. All of these circumstances can be avoided if recommended practices for usage are followed. A buffer zone several metres wide should be left by the sprayer around the edge of a field, especially where it is bounded by streams or ditches carrying water. Spray should also be kept well away from ponds or other open water bodies. This reduces the chances of damage by seepage and run-off, as well as accidental contamination by drift. Ensuring that a pesticide is used at the minimum recommended application rate also reduces the danger from run-off and percolation through the soil. Farmers should always be aware of possible alternatives to pesticides that are less potentially damaging to the wider environment. The disposal of containers and unwanted chemicals, including sheep dip, must be done following specific instructions for the particular chemical, and in accordance with relevant legislation. The Agricultural Development and Advisory Service will provide the necessary information and advice.

Fertiliser

Spreading inorganic fertilisers next to streams, ponds and ditches should also be avoided, because of the dangers of run-off causing eutrophication of the water. Leaving untreated buffer zones around field margins alongside water can reduce this possibility. In some situations, buffer zones between fields and open water can be planted with certain species of wetland plant, such as common reed or reed canary-grass, which have some capacity to remove excess nitrate and phosphate from the water.

Road run-off

Surface water draining from roads can be extremely polluting, containing much organic matter and possibly high levels of lead and zinc as well as oil. If a pond or stream receives oily water from a roadside drain, an interceptor installed in-line may help. This is essentially a stilling chamber, which allows the oil to rise to the surface and the water to be drawn off from below.

Sediments from road run-off or any other source can be removed by use of a silt-trap (see Chapter 6). Much of the heavy metal content is likely to be removed with the silt. Silt-traps and interceptors must be regularly cleaned out if they are to remain effective.

A more natural trap for sediment and some chemical pollutants may be a stand of common reed planted in shallow water at the water inlet. As well as physically trapping the particles of silt in their tangled stems and rhizomes, the reeds may help to remove organic matter and other pollutants from incoming water.

5.3   Managing vegetation

Vegetation below, above and around the water is most important for any wet habitat. If there is only sparse vegetation or none at all, planting appropriate species in the various ecological zones will enormously improve the prospects for wildlife. Planting of aquatic and bankside vegetation is covered in detail in Chapter 6.

Management of vegetation is needed because, by its very nature, it will grow and extend, and an area may eventually reach the climax of natural succession when no water remains at all. For the purposes of sustaining freshwater life, this must be prevented. The general aim is to maintain some open water while keeping a diversity of vegetation types associated with it. For flowing waters, it is necessary to prevent interference to the passage of water, especially where flood control is important. In wetland areas, as opposed to open water, the aim is to maintain the particular marsh, fen or bog flora that are so vulnerable to change and are increasingly rare.

In many situations, management operations are targeted towards cutting back and controlling aggressive, invasive species, which compete with rarer, more vulnerable and valuable species.

Control

Wetland vegetation

Marshland and wet grassland are vulnerable to invasion by scrub vegetation, which must be kept under control. This requires a cutting regime, which will have to be regularly repeated. The frequency and pattern of cutting will depend on the type of plants, the use of the land and its present conservation value. Generally, cutting should be done in late summer after flowering plants have set seed.

Grazing by livestock can be a useful management technique, and if this is an established component of the land management system, it is important to continue with it, or undesirable species will start to take over. Winter grazing will remove coarse meadow grasses, but will not affect overwintering buds of reed, for example.

Burning is a valuable management technique as long as it is done with care and consideration and in accordance with legislation. Small sections of herbaceous vegetation can be burnt off during winter. All these management options are covered more fully in *Grasslands, Heaths and Moors*.

Bankside vegetation

Planting

Generally, planting trees and scrub will enhance both the landscape and the habitat. Trees are always visually interesting, and birds, amphibians and mammals will all benefit from the cover provided by dense, scrubby vegetation. Suggested planting programmes are, however, quite different for rivers and ditches as opposed to ponds. Trees planted around a pond should not be allowed to shade the water too much, as this will reduce its productivity and cause problems from leaf fall. On the other hand, trees planted alongside a ditch or river should be positioned on the south and east side, precisely because here they will cast shade on the water, and thus reduce the growth of underwater plants that will choke the channel if left unchecked.

The particular species chosen for planting will depend on the local conditions, particularly soil type, soil pH, climate and aspect. It is also important to consider future management requirements. Table 6.1 in Chapter 6 provides some suggestions for planting.

Control

Trees at the water's edge will need some occasional management to keep them in control. Around ponds, this would be necessary to reduce shading and leaf fall, and on rivers and drainage ditches to prevent branches falling into the water where this would interfere with the flow.

Traditional management techniques for the typical bankside species of willow and alder are pollarding and coppicing, respectively. Old pollarded willows can be seen along most rivers in lowland Britain, where they are very attractive landscape features. The crown of an old pollard is a uniquely rich mini-habitat, which provides a home for other plants growing in the accumulating debris. If allowed to grow unchecked, willows tend to crack and fall over because the crown becomes top heavy. Adhering to a pollarding or coppicing regime can maintain trees in healthy condition with a lot of young growth, and may provide some income from marketing the timber. (Further details of these management techniques are given in another book in the *Practical Conservation* series: *Woodlands*.)

Management of trees and shrubs is best done on a rotation, so that at any one time there are always some mature specimens as well as those in various stages of regrowth, thus ensuring continuity of the habitat.

Leaving a heavy branch or tree trunk on the ground at or near the water's edge can enhance the habitat as long as twigs and leaves are removed from it. As it slowly rots, it will provide a home and food for many insects and fungi.

Aquatic vegetation

Control

Manual control methods include digging out, cutting and raking. These methods can be used very precisely against a particular problem species or area. They are laborious jobs, however, and may only be applicable on smaller sites or sites in areas of high conservation value where great care must be taken.

Digging out plants complete with their roots or rhizomes is a very effective method for controlling emergent species at the water's edge. Obviously, it is only possible where the water is not too deep to use a spade. Cutting is much quicker than digging, but less effective, because the roots remain and it will need to be repeated more often. Cutting the emergent plants at the

base of the stems can be done using hand tools or, in deeper water, using a chain scythe. This is a chain with cutting edges that is held at each end and dragged through the water. The cut vegetation then rises to the surface from where it can be raked off.

Raking can provide some control of most free-floating and surface plants, such as duckweeds and frogbit. A large garden rake can be used effectively, but for large areas a floating boom may be preferable. This can be a long, thin piece of wood or a heavy rope that is pulled across the surface and will collect the floating plants in front of it, especially duckweeds. Raking is unlikely to remove every bit of the plants, so regrowth will be fairly quick and the procedure will have to be repeated.

Any plant material must be removed from the site, as it will cause deoxygenation of the water if left to rot *in situ* or at the water's edge. It should be hauled temporarily onto the bank to allow excess water to drain off and, it is hoped, to allow some invertebrates to find their way back into the water. Having dried out a little, it will be easier to remove for disposal, perhaps by composting.

Mechanical control methods are much the same as manual ones, but on a larger scale. Cutting and digging out a pond or ditch can be done by excavating machinery working from the bankside, as long as the ground can support it. Vegetation control can be combined with sediment removal to keep the water open and deep. Excavators are useful for reed bed control, as they can dig out a deep channel around a stand to prevent further expansion.

Using herbicides to control aquatic vegetation is not generally recommended, but it can certainly be very effective. It is thorough, herbicides are quick to apply and quick to act, and the procedure is therefore relatively cheap. The Ministry of Agriculture, Fisheries and Food issues a list of approved chemicals for use as aquatic herbicides, and also guidelines for their use (see Appendix I). It is absolutely essential that these guidelines and all relevant legislation are followed.

Herbicides can be useful as an answer to a specific problem, for instance where a pond has been completely taken over by a single species, such as Canadian pondweed or hornwort. The plant species to be controlled must be correctly identified and the correct herbicide selected from the approved list to deal with it. After treatment, all dying plants must be removed from the water.

There is a danger that total removal of one invasive plant will leave the way open for others, especially algae, and it is possible that this may create a greater problem of control than the original one.

Control of excessive algal growth poses particular problems, as effective long-term control can only be achieved by reducing the nutrient content of the water. However, recent research has shown that a natural algicide is produced by rotting straw as it decomposes. This means that effective control of algae in a lake or pond can be achieved cheaply and simply by putting straw in the water. Only a small quantity of straw is needed, approximately 10 grams per cubic metre of water, which should be applied twice a year, in autumn and spring, because the effects only appear to last about six months.

Table 5.1 lists several species that may cause management difficulties.

Table 5.1 Aquatic plants that may need control and the appropriate methods of control

Name of plant	Main method of spread	Recommended control method	Acceptable alternative methods
1 *Free-floating*			
Blue-green algae ('algal blooms')	Cell division	None*	None
Duckweeds	Budding	Raking[†]	None
Filamentous algae	Cell division	Straw	Raking or dragging[†]
2 *Submerged, rooted*			
Canadian pondweed	Roots, stem fragments	Cutting and hoeing	Digging
Mare's-tail	Rhizomes	Cutting and hoeing	Digging
3 *Floating-leaved*			
Water-lilies	Rhizomes, rhizome fragments	Digging or pulling up	Cutting[†]
4 *Emergent*			
Branched bur-reed	Rhizomes, seeds	Digging	Cutting, Dalapon[‡]
Common reed	Rhizomes	Dalapon	Digging, cutting
Reed sweet-grass	Rhizomes	Digging	Mowing,[§] Dalapon
Great reedmace	Rhizomes	Digging	Dalapon, cutting
Rush	Rhizomes, seeds	Digging	Mowing[§]
Yellow flag	Rhizomes, seeds	Digging	Cutting

(Source: Adapted from British Trust for Conservation Volunteers/Brooks, 1981)

*This plant indicates highly nutrified water and can be prevented from causing problems, in the long run, only by controlling the inflow of nutrients.

[†]Short-term control only.

[‡]Dalapon is a recommended species-selective herbicide.

[§]When growing in fairly dry conditions.

5.4 *Managing wildlife*

The various management options described in this chapter will do a great deal to encourage all forms of wildlife. In addition, there are possibilities for habitat enhancement directed at particular animals, especially fish, birds and mammals.

The general needs of fish have been covered in Chapters 3 and 4. If these needs are met and a good habitat for fish already exists, this should be maintained. In a river, the most important factors are the retention of riffles

Fish

Table 5.2 Characteristics of major bird species breeding in close association with rivers

Species	Status	Habitat characteristics	Food	Comments
Great crested grebe	Uncommon, mainly in south	Deep; lake-like; quiet; well-developed fringing emergent vegetation especially reeds	Fish; aquatic invertebrates	Nests of vegetation attached to reeds or trailing branches
Little grebe	Widespread and sometimes numerous, especially in south	Luxuriant aquatic, emergent and marginal vegetation, overhanging branches, bushes and scrub	Insects; molluscs; tadpoles; small fish	Floating nest platforms attached to emergent vegetation, trailing branches
Mallard	Very common and widespread	Emergent vegetation; bankside scrub; rank herbage; old willows. Very adaptable	Omnivorous and opportunistic	Where habitat on river banks is not ideal will freely nest at distance from water, up ditches, in hedges or scrub. Young then brought to water
Tufted duck	Locally common	Open lake-like sections with good marginal emergent vegetation	Omnivorous: fish; aquatic invertebrates; green plant material	Nests in tussocks or dense aquatic vegetation. Apparent territories on rivers may involve birds actually nesting on nearby lakes, pools or gravel pits
Red-breasted merganser	Widespread in north and west of Scotland; spreading in northern England and Wales	Well-oxygenated, unpolluted upland rivers, with boulders, riffles and sand banks. Banks with dense vegetation such as heather, scrub or woodland	Fish	Preference for coastal areas. Nests in dense ground cover
Goosander	Highlands; south-west Scotland and northern England; spreading in Wales	Clear, unpolluted, upland rivers, particularly where well wooded	Fish	More inland and montane than merganser. Prefers to nest in tree holes over or close to water
Mute swan	Widespread in lowland areas; numerous in south	Wide or open channels with islands, backwaters, spits or stands of emergent vegetation, e.g. reeds	Mainly aquatic vegetation, also emergent plants and seeds. Also graze on land, particularly early in season	Former declines on rivers in parts of England were attributed to effects of lead. Populations now recovering. Local distribution changes attributable to effects of navigation or increased availability of other habitat, e.g. gravel pits
Moorhen	Very common and widespread	Abundant emergent vegetation, bankside scrub, overhanging trees, bushes or hedgerows	Omnivorous; may feed within river but also often in adjacent pasture	Nests in emergent vegetation, trailing branches or in bushes. May nest well away from river if suitable habitat is lacking
Sand martin	Widespread; less so in south	Vertical earth and sand banks soft enough for burrowing. Open areas without woodland	Aerial insects	Colonies vary from year to year, sites being unstable and liable to become unsuitable. Opportunistic and may nest in pipes in walls

Species	Status	Habitat characteristics	Food	Comments
Coot	Common and widespread in south; more scarce in north	Moderately wide, open channels, with extensive marginal emergent vegetation, such as reeds and bulrushes. Overhanging and trailing scrub or branches important for early nests	Omnivorous; plants predominant	Nests floating or over water in rushes, reeds or trailing branches. Adjacent wet pasture may be important for feeding early in season
Common sandpiper	Widespread in upland areas north of line from Humber to Severn estuaries	Well-oxygenated; rocky, shingle shores, banks and islands; rough vegetation on or near to river	Aquatic invertebrates	Nests in rough cover on the river bank, islands or some distance away, usually well above normal flood levels
Kingfisher	Widespread and quite common except in Scotland where scarce and mainly found south of the Highlands	Exposed earthbanks, usually overhanging water; requires perches, e.g. branches, coarse vegetation, from which to fish. Usually in relatively open sections	Mainly fish but also tadpoles and aquatic invertebrates	Nests usually in earthbanks; may nest away from river or in tree roots
Dipper	Widespread in north and west; absent from England east of line from Humber to Isle of Wight	Turbulent, well-oxygenated streams and rivers; rocks, boulders, shingle, waterfalls; rock outcrops; earthbanks. Open moorland or wooded sections	Aquatic invertebrates taken on or below water surface	Nests naturally on rock outcrops or in earthbank overhangs and tree rocks; regular use of man-made structures such as bridges and weirs
Reed warbler	Widespread in south; absent from north England, Scotland and much of Wales	Beds of reed; reed fringe or other rough bankside vegetation (willowherb, hawthorn)	Predominantly insectivorous	Large numbers usually confined to extensive reed beds, but scattered pairs elsewhere. Nests typically attached to reed stems, well above ground or water level
Sedge warbler	Widespread and numerous throughout lowland Britain	Reeds, willow carr, hawthorn thickets, rough scrub and bushes	Insectivorous	Nests low down in dense vegetation
Grey wagtail	Widespread, though absent from much of central and eastern England	Turbulent upland streams; weirs; mill races. Rock outcrops	Insectivorous	Nests on rocky ledges; in tree roots; also on man-made structures
Reed bunting	Widespread and common	Marshy areas; reed beds; fringing emergent vegetation; hedgerows and ditches; rank vegetation		Nests in thick vegetation. Formerly largely restricted to marsh or riverine areas; has now spread widely into rough ground in agricultural areas

(Source: Adapted from Lewis and Williams, 1984)

and pools, patches of aquatic plants and overhanging bankside vegetation. If channel work requires the removal of vegetation, it is important that some areas are left undisturbed, so that the fish have a refuge while the work is in progress. The timing of weed-cutting is also important, as cutting in early summer can remove plants on which perch, pike or roach have laid their eggs.

Habitat enhancement for fish on rivers can be achieved by building fish shelters. These are artificial overhangs constructed on the bank either above or below water level, which provide shade and cover from predators.

Birds

Access to water, shelter, mixed vegetation, sources of food and availability of nesting sites are all important habitat features for birds. Table 5.2 gives details of the distribution and habitat characteristics of major species breeding in or near rivers.

Most water birds nest on the ground or within emergent vegetation. They are therefore very vulnerable to disturbance by people and domestic animals, both livestock and pets, as well as to their natural predators, such as crows, rats, foxes and mink. Dense vegetation at the water's edge provides cover for many species. Ducks prefer tall, tussocky herbaceous plants and also shrubby cover. Mallard nest particularly early in the season, often before new growth begins, so the dead stems of plants such as nettles and willowherb from the previous season should be left to provide some cover for these early nests.

Once the young birds have hatched, they need easy access to the water, so banks must not be steep. In addition, they like shallow water, with some shelter from winds and protection from fast-flowing water. Shallow bays around lakes and ponds provide good conditions for many young water birds. Islands give good protection from disturbance, but also need to have gently shelving banks and an indented outline if possible. A mixture of water plants, both submerged and emergent, will ensure a varied population of invertebrates, which is essential for the diet required by the growing young.

Some birds have very specific requirements for nest sites, and artificial nest tunnels and boxes can be built for particular species, such as kingfishers, sand martins, shelduck, dippers and grey wagtails. Information and advice can be obtained from the Royal Society for the Protection of Birds.

Mammals

Maintaining a good habitat for aquatic mammals greatly depends on retention of bankside vegetation, which all three native species (otter, water shrew, water vole) need for cover. Table 5.3 has further details of the habitat preferences and distribution of mammal species associated with rivers.

Water shrews and voles are small and easily hidden, so their demands for cover are less exacting than otters, which need near-continuous river bank vegetation over an extensive area. Tree and shrub removal must be kept to a minimum, and disturbance of known holt sites should be avoided at all costs. Entrances to holts are sometimes found among the roots of mature oak, ash and sycamore where these are exposed on the riverbank. These trees are likely to be considered potential flood hazards and therefore targeted for removal. The trees can be retained, while still achieving the necessary flood protection, by shielding the bank from the force of the current to avoid further erosion, or by trimming the trees to reduce the likelihood of their falling.

Table 5.3 Preferred habitats and distribution of mammals particularly associated with rivers

Common name	Habitat	Distribution	Food sources	Comments
Otter	Rivers and wetlands exclusively. Needs cover of marginal vegetation, trees and reed beds. Secure breeding sites essential	Now largely absent from central and south England and South Wales. Only abundant in north-west Highlands and islands of Scotland	Predominantly fish, particularly eels. Frogs and occasionally young birds and mammals	*Protected species.* Nocturnal
Mink (non-native)	Rivers and wetlands, with cover of marginal vegetation and/or trees	Became established in the late 1950s, now widespread and still expanding	Crayfish, fish, birds and their eggs, small mammals, large insects	Now thought not to be competing with otter. Mainly nocturnal
Water shrew	Clear, unpolluted streams and wetlands, with plant cover	Throughout Britain	Insects predominantly, also small fish, snails and frogs	Small burrows in banks near surface. Active day and night
Water vole	Lowland rivers, canals, ponds and drainage ditches with clay banks and good marginal vegetation	Throughout Britain	Water plants; very selective feeder	Small burrows in banks (and pastures) near surface. Semi-colonial. Day-active
Natterer's bat	Open woodland and grassland, particularly over rivers	Throughout Britain, no longer common	Moths; dusk-flying insects	*Protected species.* Nocturnal. Roosts in old trees in summer, and sometimes in winter
Daubenton's bat	Over reed beds and rivers, with marginal vegetation and trees	Throughout Britain, no longer common	Moths; dusk-flying insects	*Protected species.* Nocturnal, roosts in hollow trees

(Source: Lewis and Williams, 1984)

Enhancing the habitat for otters can be achieved by planting trees close to water and encouraging saplings that could form future holt sites, as well as by building artificial holts, as long as general cover and food supply is adequate. More information on artificial holts and all aspects of conservation for otters can be obtained from the Otters and Rivers Project, c/o The Royal Society for Nature Conservation, The Green, Nettleham, Lincoln LN2 2NR.

The bats most frequently associated with fresh water – Daubenton's bat and Natterer's bat – feed on insects flying over and emerging from the water, so their interests are served by maintaining a good habitat for aquatic invertebrates, with diverse types of vegetation and clean water. For roost sites, they make use of holes, cracks and crevices in old and hollow trees, and these must be retained wherever possible. Further information on bat conservation can be obtained from the Bat Conservation Trust, c/o The Conservation Foundation, 1 Kensington Gore, London SW7 2AR.

5.5 Managing access

All water and wetland habitats are attractive places to visit, all the more so if imaginative and successful management has encouraged birds and other wildlife. This may create a problem, as the presence of people can disturb the very animals that they have come to see. Keeping people away altogether may benefit the wildlife, but in most situations this is not practical. In urban areas or near to a public Right of Way it may be impossible, and where access is essential to a commercial interest, such as angling, watersports or shooting, it may be undesirable. Whatever the circumstance, access should be managed to minimise disturbance, while still allowing recreational activities, as well as wildlife conservation, to continue.

Encouraging limited access to a site may be better than trying to keep people away completely. Exclusion is only likely to make them curious and could cause more harm than good. Arranging nature trails and providing information on display boards or in leaflets can satisfy the needs of nature lovers, and at the same time keep them away from particularly sensitive areas. Most people keep to paths as long as these are clearly marked and maintained. Dense vegetation will deter almost anybody, so planting uncomfortable species like holly and bramble in strategic places can form a good barrier against the inquisitive explorer. Fencing will do the same job, but is more obtrusive and more expensive.

At popular locations, the environment may be best served by providing car parking facilities, even where this means flattening an area for hard standing. With sensitive design, the impact may well be less than that of indiscriminate parking on soft verges or elsewhere. Provision for the public may need to include litter bins and possibly toilets, which will require servicing on a regular and continuing basis.

On lakes and reservoirs, which meet several different demands, zoning of the activities can be successful. Separate areas or zones of the water body can be designated for a particular purpose, so that conflict between users is kept to a minimum. For example, windsurfers and water-skiers can make use of one area and anglers another, while a third is left undisturbed, except perhaps for birdwatchers' hides. Box 5.1 shows an example of reservoir zoning.

5.6 Options for managing your water and wetland habitats

The exercise and case study sections related to this chapter are in Sections 6.6 and 6.7 respectively in Chapter 6.

Box 5.1 Reservoir zoning at Grafham Water

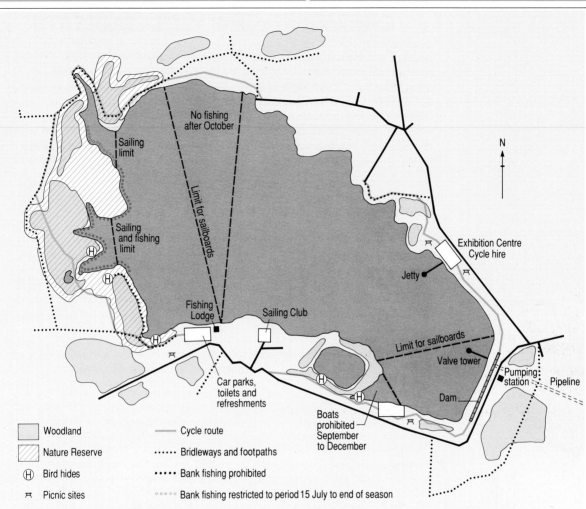

Woodland
Nature Reserve
(H) Bird hides
⚲ Picnic sites

Cycle route
...... Bridleways and footpaths
•••• Bank fishing prohibited
ₒₒₒₒₒ Bank fishing restricted to period 15 July to end of season

Grafham Water is a water supply reservoir covering 600 hectares near Huntingdon. It has been zoned to allow the integration of wildlife conservation and several different leisure activities with the primary function of the reservoir, which is to store water prior to treatment and distribution. Many people visit the reservoir, for windsurfing, sailing, fly-fishing, cycling, nature trails, birdwatching or simply to enjoy a picnic by the water's edge. Three car parks, each with toilets, refreshments and a children's play area, provide the necessary facilities for the numerous visitors. The main part of the reservoir is available to all users. In two smaller zones, sailboards are prohibited but sailing and boat fishing are permitted. The sheltered bays at the western end are wildlife sanctuaries where no windsurfing or sailing is allowed. In the more southerly of the two, fising boats and bank fishing are also prohibited to provide an area completely free of disturbance. Access to this area from land is carefully controlled by clearly way-marking footpaths, bridleways and cycle routes, in order to protect the wildlife further. (Source: Anglian Water plc leaflets.)

Chapter 6

CREATING NEW WET HABITATS

Most of the wet habitats found in Britain cannot be created easily. Peat bogs, for example, take many centuries for the layers of rotting vegetation to accumulate. Features such as rivers and streams are components of the natural landscape that have developed through geological time. On the other hand, the creation of ponds and lakes is something that can be achieved with remarkably rapid development of a rich habitat for wildlife. In fact, of all habitats that the wildlife enthusiast might consider creating, ponds probably provide the quickest return on the investment in terms of wildlife value.

The main questions to consider from a conservation point of view when creating new wet habitats are:

▶   which sites should or should not be developed;

▶   how any species already present on the site can be protected;

▶   how a pond or lake with the capacity to become rich in wildlife can be created;

▶   how a pond or lake can be planned and designed to blend in with the landscape;

▶   how ponds or lakes designed for angling, recreation and other uses can also provide valuable wildlife habitats and landscape features.

Before starting work on a new pond, you must be certain that any regulations or legislation have been complied with and that you have consulted and gained permission from the relevant authorities. Further details can be found in the *Legislation and Regulations* booklet in the foundation module.

6.1   Site selection

Position in the landscape

Taking a broad view, consider where a new pond will create an interesting focal point in the landscape, and the possible viewpoints from which it can be appreciated. It should not be too close to buildings, because of the potential disturbance from people and animals, as seclusion is very important for wildlife. Buildings and yards are also a potential source of pollution from rainwater run-off.

Consideration of the habitat diversity of the surrounding area is necessary. A variety of habitats in the vicinity will improve the potential of a new pond. Some dense undergrowth and scrub will provide essential refuge for many water birds and animals. Conversely, a pond may attract species that are normally resident in nearby woods, for example to come and take water. Many aquatic species will colonise a new pond from existing water bodies if the intervening distance is not too great. Wet ditches and streams can act as corridors for these migrating species, and increase colonisation from one site to another.

Although nearby woodland is an overall advantage, it is important that a pond is not overhung with branches or shaded by tall trees. It is especially important that the south side is open, to maximise the sunlight available to aquatic and bankside plants. Trees and shrubs of any appreciable size should be confined to the north and west sides of a pond.

Of utmost importance in site selection is avoiding the destruction of an existing valuable site by digging it up to make a new pond. Expert advice should be sought if there is any doubt as to the existing wildlife value of the location.

Practical considerations

Ponds can be divided into three categories: on-stream, off-stream and non-stream fed. On-stream and off-stream ponds, as illustrated in Figure 6.1, have a running water supply from a stream or spring. Non-stream fed ponds are those sustained by rainwater or groundwater where there is a high water table.

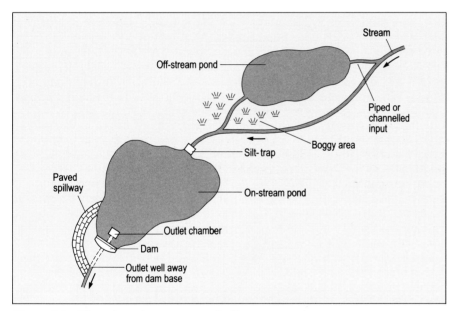

Figure 6.1   *Plan view of on-stream and off-stream ponds.*
(Source: British Association for Shooting and Conservation, undated)

In any situation, the water supply must be clean and reliable. Running water has the advantage that a constant supply of fresh, oxygenated water flows into the pond and prevents it becoming stagnant. On the other hand, streams may be polluted and care should be taken to look at the surrounding land upstream in the catchment area to locate potential sources of pollution. The supply needs to be reliable throughout the year, even in prolonged dry weather. The quantity available needs to be estimated to ensure that there is sufficient to sustain the proposed pond and for determining the requirements for the inlet and outlet. If the water level in the pond is to be maintained from a high water table, observation or knowledge over several seasons is needed to ensure that the water table remains high throughout the summer.

A detailed topographical survey of the location is essential on large sites, and where water level control devices must be constructed at the inlet and outlet. This requires the use of surveyor's equipment to chart the levels of the land. For smaller sites, levels can be estimated more simply. Find a piece of transparent hose long enough to lie across the proposed longest axis of the pond. Fill the hose with water, ensuring that there are no air bubbles, lay the hose across the site and hold the ends vertically. The water in the hose will be at the same level at both ends. Mark the level on pegs stuck in the ground. Then move one end to another point approximately on the planned perimeter of the pond and mark the water level again on a peg. Repeat this to mark the water level at several points all round the proposed pond site. The resulting series of pegs will mark a horizontal plane from which to gauge the extent and outline of the pond when it is full of water.

You need to know the answer to the question: 'Will the pond hold water?' Background information gathered for landscape and habitat assessment will have included geology and soil type. Soil texture can be identified by hand. A small amount of moist soil should be taken and worked in the hand. Clay soils feel smooth, can be moulded easily and will smear or polish when rubbed. If the soil feels rough or gritty and cannot be rolled into a ball, this indicates a sandy soil. If the soil type is uniform over a wide area, it will have little influence on your pond site selection, except possibly to deter you from building a pond at all. Sands and gravels will not hold water unless there is a high water table. Clay soils are best for retaining water, but some profiles may be interleaved with gravel lenses, particularly in river valley deposits. The only reliable way to answer the question about water retention in advance is to dig trial pits. There should be at least two pits within the potential pond area, more if the pond is large or if the soil type is known to vary. The pits should be dug in pairs to a depth similar to the planned pond depth, which ideally should be 2–3 metres. One should be filled with water and the other left empty and allowed to fill of its own accord. The pits should be monitored over several days, preferably longer. If the water rapidly drains away, the ground will not hold water, and a liner of some sort will be needed (see Section 6.3). If the water level remains static, the clay content is probably sufficient to hold water unaided. If the trial pits show both rising and falling levels, this indicates a fluctuating water table, which may make the use of a flexible liner difficult. Trial pits will also provide the necessary information on reliability of the water table, where this is the intended water supply. To assess seasonal variations in water table, monitoring of the pits must continue for 12 months. If the empty hole fills with water but does so very slowly, this suggests that the soil permeability is low, but that establishing a pond in this way is possible. If the empty hole remains empty, this indicates that the water table is not high enough to create a pond, unless deeper excavation is undertaken. Digging trial pits also allows a visual inspection and assessment of the soil type right down to the maximum intended pond depth.

The available water source and the topography will determine whether you build an on-stream or off-stream pond. An on-stream pond can only be created by blocking a watercourse with a bank or dam, which can be complicated, and expensive. An on-stream pond is also more likely to be troubled by problems caused by siltation and water turbidity, and by erosion at the inlet.

To design a dam and outlet, it is necessary to calculate the average discharge or base flow of the river, so that the structures can be sized correctly. The outlet must be big enough to accommodate five times the base flow. In addition, it is necessary to calculate potential flood flows. These are derived from the size of the catchment area and the annual rainfall. A dam must be designed and built with a spillway or other overflow device to allow flood waters to bypass it without causing damage to it or surrounding land and property.

If no alternative to an on-stream design is possible, you must ensure that the legal requirements of the Reservoirs Act 1975 are met, and consult an engineer and/or ensure that your dam and overflow are adequately sized for flood flows.

Off-stream and non-stream fed ponds are generally much easier to build and maintain. They do not necessarily need dams, with all their attendant difficulties, and they are less liable to siltation.

Avoid any site that is known to be or to have been land drained, as this will cause great problems even when a liner is used. Check the site for any service pipes and cables, such as telephone, electricity or gas, as these will need to be avoided. Above ground, pylons and telegraph poles may interfere with bird flight lines or fishing rods and also should be avoided.

6.2   Designing a wildlife-rich pond

Size and shape

In general, large ponds will have a greater potential for a variety of different habitats than small ponds, so one could say for the size of a new pond, the larger the better. However, this should not be interpreted as as large as possible. If the total space available for a pond is limited, for example a field corner bounded by existing hedges, then it is important not to fill all the space with water. There should be a buffer zone between the water's edge and the surrounding land, in which vegetation is allowed to develop, otherwise the wildlife potential will be severely reduced. Small ponds can also be very valuable, especially if close to other good wildlife habitats.

The outline of a pond should be irregular, with spits and bays, as illustrated in Figure 6.2 (overleaf). This increases the length of shoreline for the growth of emergent and rooted aquatic plants, and provides more locations for birds for feeding and sheltered places suitable for roosting and nesting. The same basic design features apply, even if the encouragement of waterfowl for shooting is not an intended purpose for the pond.

Once the size and shape has been decided, mark out the intended shoreline with pegs. These should be spaced close enough to each other that spits and bays are clearly identifiable when it comes to digging the hole for the pond.

Islands

Islands can provide additional sites of refuge in new water bodies, but they are best in larger ponds or lakes. To be completely safe for birds, there should be a minimum distance of 30 metres from the island to the shore, to prevent predators such as weasels and stoats from reaching the island to attack nests. If this distance is not possible, an island can still have some advantages, as it will provide protection from disturbance by humans and

91

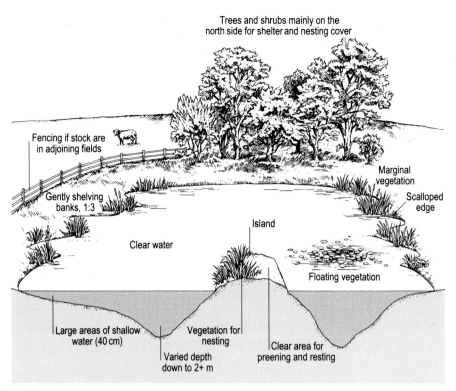

Trees and shrubs mainly on the
north side for shelter and nesting cover

Fencing if stock are
in adjoining fields

Gently shelving
banks, 1:3

Clear water

Marginal
vegetation

Scalloped
edge

Island

Floating vegetation

Large areas of shallow
water (40 cm)

Vegetation for
nesting

Clear area for
preening and resting

Varied depth
down to 2+ m

*Figure 6.2   Main design features to be included in a shooting/conservation pond.
(Source: British Association for Shooting and Conservation, undated)*

some animals. It is also important that creating an island does not mean that
the deep parts of the pond have to be made shallower. It is more important
to maintain an area of deep, open water than it is to provide an island.

The shape of the island should ideally be that of a crescent or Maltese Cross
to provide a long shoreline with sheltered areas. On large water bodies,
consider the direction of the prevailing wind and position the island to offer
the best protection from it.

Artificial islands can be created to provide nesting sites for water birds by
building rafts to be permanently moored in the pond. These rafts should
float with the deck just above water level. They must be stable, must provide
dry, sheltered, accessible nest sites and must be able to support their own
vegetation to provide cover and to blend in with the surroundings. The size,
design and construction materials will depend on the size of the pond and
the species of bird to be housed. Further details on artificial islands can be
obtained from the British Trust for Conservation Volunteers (see Appendix I).

Depth and profile

A pond should reach a depth of at least 2 metres and preferably more. This
prevents the spread of emergent vegetation and ensures an area of permanent open water. It also reduces the likelihood of the pond drying out
during dry weather or being completely frozen in winter. The profile of the
pond should have a variation in depth from the deepest area through to very
shallow. Shelf areas at different depths beneath the water provide surfaces

92

where different plants can find purchase for their roots (see Chapter 3). A broad shelf at a depth of between 1.5 and 2.5 centimetres, extending at least 1 metre into the pond, particularly around the bays, provides the very shallow zone that is necessary for many marsh plants. Another shelf at somewhere between 0.5 and 1 metre deep will be colonised by emergent marginal vegetation. Floating-leaved and submerged plants will root on flat areas at a depth of between 1 and 3 metres, where emergent species do not compete with them. If the pond is large enough, extensive areas around 2 metres deep will attract diving ducks, such as pochard and tufted duck.

Steep sides should be avoided, if wildlife is to be encouraged. A very gentle slope into the water is required, to allow access for many birds and animals. Ducklings can only manage a step of about 5 centimetres from land to water. This should be remembered when constructing an island, as it too should have a gentle slope into the water.

Farm reservoirs designed for holding irrigation water inevitably suffer great fluctuation in depth as the water is drawn off in the summer. Deep, excavated pools in the pond should ensure that some water persists throughout the year, allowing fish and invertebrates to survive.

Creating marshy areas adjacent to a pond will attract other species, particularly wading birds. Shallow, sloping pond edges can be extended in one or two areas to create flat marshland that blends into the pond. This will provide the right environment for plants that like damp conditions but can survive seasonal drying, such as marsh marigold.

In sandy soils, it may be possible to have a small cliff at the water's edge at one side of the pond. This would provide nesting sites for sand martins and kingfishers. The cliff should rise about 1.2 metres above the surface of the water and preferably be on the west or east side of the pond.

Anglers prefer steep banks to give access to deep water a rod's length from the bankside. Some steep and some gradual banks should provide for all requirements. Alternatively, the anglers' needs can be met by building piers out into the deep water or using pontoons.

Inlet and outlet

The inlet to an off-stream pond is usually a pipe or ditch diverting some of the stream flow into the pond. It is important that sufficient water remains in the main channel to sustain it. The pipe or ditch should be fitted with a control valve of some sort, such as a sluice gate or drop-board, to control the quantity of water taken off. Piped inlets are best placed pointing downstream, so that water has to flow round a corner into the pond. This significantly reduces the quantity of sediment washing into the pond, and therefore the need for dredging.

For on-stream ponds, the inlet should incorporate a silt-trap. When a watercourse opens out into a pond, the flow rate suddenly decreases and the sediment carried by the flowing water is deposited on the bottom. This sediment accumulates at the pond inlet and will gradually reduce the depth and capacity of the pond. To remove it requires extensive dredging on a regular basis. A silt-trap consists of a stilling chamber with an overflow into the pond itself, and confines the sediment in one small area, making it much easier to deal with. The trap must be sized according to the discharge of the stream and its sediment load and should be cleared out regularly.

The outlet from an off-stream pond must have greater capacity than the inlet, to prevent the pond flooding over its banks and to conduct the overflow back into the stream. Non-stream fed ponds may also need an outlet pipe to contain and direct overflow after heavy rain.

Large ponds and lakes that are managed for birds will benefit from a level control facility at the outlet point that allows the water to be drawn down to expose the mud in the shallows. This can attract many species of waders at certain times of year.

6.3   Pond construction

Constructing dams

Dams are not easy to build, as great care is needed to ensure stability and water-tightness. Except for very small dams, the design and construction should be supervised by a qualified civil engineer. Small on-stream ponds can be created by building a bank no more than 1 metre high across the stream, but these are of limited value as they are unlikely to be very deep and will silt up rapidly.

Excavation

Excavating the hole in the ground for a new pond can be done by manual labour, using shovels, buckets and wheelbarrows. This is obviously only practical for small ponds, and even then it is a case where many hands do not make particularly light work. Using machinery is much quicker, but may incur greater cost.

Mechanical diggers for the purpose are of two types: hydraulic excavators and cranes. Excavators such as JCB and Hy-mac have an articulated hydraulic arm with a scoop on the end. Cranes have a jib with a bucket on the end of a line, hence they are usually called draglines. Draglines are normally only appropriate for long-term projects, as the additional cost of transporting them to site must be considered. Hydraulic excavators may be wheeled or run on caterpillar tracks and are generally more transportable. They can also be operated with greater precision.

Heavy machinery will cause compaction of the soil beneath it. To minimise this damage, it is advisable to mark clearly the area within which the digger can manoeuvre, using pegs or tape.

The driver/operator must be given clear instructions on the required boundaries, depths and profile of the pond. Discussion with the operator before work starts should clarify the details of the plan, such as the stepped nature of the underwater profile or the need for gentle slopes at the water's edge. The site should be clearly marked out on the ground to avoid misunderstanding. With skilled manipulation, it is possible for a digger to construct surprisingly small and delicate features. In addition to the digging machinery, it may be necessary to use a pump to remove water from the hole during digging. This is most likely where there is a high water table. Dragline machinery can be used underwater if pumping is impractical.

An island can be created by leaving an area untouched during excavation, remembering to slope the sides gradually. Alternatively, an island can be built by piling rubble into the middle of the pond. This may need to be confined by a ring of stakes driven into the ground and can then be topped off with soil.

Spoil disposal

Spoil disposal after pond construction or clearance can be a problem. When the hole is being dug, the topsoil should be taken off first and piled separately from the subsoil. Some of the topsoil can be used to give the new pond a good start by putting a layer 15–20 centimetres deep back into the newly excavated hole, before it is flooded. This can be done whether the pond has a liner or not. The topsoil provides a good rooting medium for plants, since it already contains nutrients, and also provides a substrate for burrowing aquatic invertebrates. The practice is less appropriate in upland areas where fresh water is naturally oligotrophic, because the topsoil may make the new pond too rich in nutrients. Similarly, in intensively farmed areas, because of soil enrichment problems it is best to cover the pond bed with small patches of topsoil, in total no greater than 25 per cent of the area.

The possible options for spoil disposal are to spread it over surrounding land or to use it for landfill or landscaping. A thin layer of soil can be spread over surrounding land and in time will incorporate into the ground. Larger quantities can be disposed of by landfill in appropriate places, such as worked-out quarries. However, in both these cases, great care must be taken to ensure that no damage is caused to another habitat by doing this. It is inadvisable, for example, to use the spoil to fill in small hollows in old grassland, as these may have rich plant communities.

In some locations, soil can be formed into banks, which should have gentle contours to look natural, and then be grassed over or otherwise planted. Spreading the separated topsoil over a subsoil embankment will improve the chances of successful planting. Building embankments in this way can be a bonus, if they are used to hide ugly buildings, or as a buffer between a pond and a busy road or intensively cultivated arable field.

In other circumstances, it may be necessary to transport the spoil by truck or tractor and trailer to an appropriate disposal site elsewhere, although the disposal options at the new site remain the same.

All options – spreading, landfill or landscaping – will incur time and therefore money for the use of the heavy machinery over and above that required for excavating a hole. Transporting the spoil before disposal adds to the problem. These additional costs should not be underestimated.

Linings

Lining a pond to make it hold water inevitably adds to the problems and costs incurred in pond creation. If site tests have indicated that a lining will be required, it may be worth reconsidering for a moment whether building a pond in that particular location is the best course of action to take. Artificial liners are generally only appropriate for smaller ponds, say less than 10 metres in diameter, because pieces of liner are difficult to join together for larger areas and the cost may become prohibitive. The use of artificial liners also tends to dictate a simpler outline than the recommended spits and bays.

The traditional form of pond lining is puddled clay. This consists of a layer of clay covering the bottom of the pond, which is worked when wet (puddled) into soft mud; this is then carefully layered and sets into an impermeable layer. If it has been decided that a lining is necessary, then it follows that the clay will probably have to be imported to the site. The distance and ease of transportation and the resulting cost must be considered before this is undertaken. Puddling can be done by foot, or rather feet, but it is a tedious process. It can also be done by using a tractor or tracked machinery to distribute the clay around the pond bottom, as long as the operator has the appropriate training and experience. It is important that clay-lined ponds are never allowed to dry out or they may crack and then leak.

Bentonite clay is a naturally occurring mineral which, on wetting, swells to 10–20 times its dry volume. It can be mixed with permeable soil to make an impermeable layer for lining a new pond. The amount needed depends on the nature of the soil with which it will be mixed, and advice can be obtained from the suppliers who market it. It can also be used for repairing leaking ponds.

Various impermeable sheeting materials are available for use as artificial pond liners. They can be classified into three groups: polythene, PVC and butyl rubber. The cheapest of these is polythene, but it has a limited lifespan unless completely covered by soil to a depth of approximately 30 centimetres. PVC is more expensive and longer lasting, but also requires soil cover. Butyl rubber is the most expensive and may be too costly for larger projects.

The ground must be carefully prepared before laying an artificial liner. Slopes should be as gentle as possible. Rocks and sharp objects that might tear the liner must be removed. If the ground is so stony that this is an impossible task, a thick layer of soft material must be laid under the liner. This could be sand or soil, or small ponds can be padded with fine ash, sawdust or thick layers of wet newspaper.

When calculating the size of the lining material required, it must be remembered that the area to be covered on the bottom of the pond is larger than the final surface area of the water. Like putting a pastry lining in a deep pie dish, a generous allowance should be left all round. This must be sufficient to allow for securing and hiding the edge of the liner. Any excess can always be cut off, but new edge pieces cannot be stuck on. When laying a PVC or polythene liner in hot weather, even more slack must be allowed as these materials will contract on cooling. They can be folded into darts around the edges; butyl rubber should not be folded. For larger ponds, polythene sheets can be joined together with adhesive and tape. PVC and butyl rubber are usually made to the right size in advance. Once filled with water, the lining must be securely anchored around the edge, usually by burying it in a trench. To allow plants to grow in and around the pond, a layer of soil should be spread on top of the liner. This is in any case essential for polythene and PVC liners which are weakened by sunlight. A layer at least 30 centimetres deep is recommended.

Concrete is another possible lining material, which has been used in the past for garden ponds and also for making new dew ponds. As well as having an unnatural appearance, it tends to crack and decay over the years and is not recommended.

6.4 Colonisation and introduction of plants and animals

Vegetation

Once a pond has been created, it needs some vegetation before it will have any appeal to birds and animals. Some plants, if present in the vicinity, will colonise naturally, but this is a slow process. Planting appropriate examples of aquatic and bankside plants will rapidly create conditions that look natural and encourage other forms of wildlife. Natural colonisation will, of course, continue, but planting desirable species reduces the likelihood of one or two particularly aggressive species becoming dominant.

Like starting a new garden from scratch, the planting of the pond should be carefully planned. Draw a sketch map of the area around the pond and mark onto it the existing structures, trees and other plants. Then add the areas for new planting in and around the water; include the types of plant that you intend to use and, depending on the scale of the map, possibly individual specimens. It is not necessary to plant very many of each aquatic species as they tend to establish and spread quite quickly as long as conditions are suitable.

As in garden planting, if you want the result to look natural, avoid straight lines and plant in clumps. For larger projects, consultation with a landscape architect may be helpful.

There are several points to consider when selecting plants for a new pond. The most important is to chose native species, not introduced or exotic varieties. Native species are better value for wildlife as they support greater numbers of invertebrates. The species chosen should be found locally, be known to thrive in the area and they should be appropriate for the specific conditions that are found in the pond, for instance the pH of the water, the type of substrate and the depth of the water. Extensive lists of the conditions preferred by individual species can be found in several reference books. Table 6.1 (overleaf) provides a selection of plants recommended for planting. Some conditions may be difficult to forecast for a new pond, for example the nutrient content of the water will change as the pond develops. Looking at similar ponds nearby will provide some clue as to the likely outcome.

Plant selection

As for all aspects of habitat creation, it is a variety of different plants that will provide the best opportunities for wildlife. A planting plan should therefore include some plants for each zone of the pond, particularly emergents and floating aquatics, as well as bankside planting of trees, bushes, and possibly grasses and herbs.

If a pond has other possible uses as well as wildlife conservation, it is important to choose plant species that are compatible with these other uses. For example, water-lilies and other floating-leaved plants are not viewed with delight by anglers, so these should be avoided in ponds and lakes intended for use as fisheries.

Plant sources

There are two options for obtaining the necessary plants. They can either be bought from a shop or garden centre or, preferably, transferred from an existing site in the locality. The latter option probably provides a better chance of success and is obviously cheaper, but some guidelines must be followed. By law, the landowner of the donor pond must be consulted and his or her permission obtained before any plants are removed. It would be

Table 6.1 Recommended species for planting in and around new ponds

Species	General comments	Value to wildfowl and other wildlife	Height range
Trees and shrubs			
Alder	Wet soils. Improves poor soils through nitrogen fixation. Fast growing. Coppices well	Seeds eaten by mallard and teal. Screens and shelters ponds. Nesting cover. 141 associated invertebrate species	15–20 m
Willow	Wet soils. Coppices well. Easily propagated from cuttings and grows rapidly	Screens and shelters ponds. High insect value – over 250 associated invertebrates. Nesting cover	
Goat willow	Grows as bushy shrub		3–10 m
Grey willow (Common sallow)	Grows as bushy shrub		2–10 m
Crack willow	Tall, bankside tree		20 m+
Oak	Requires drier soils, therefore plant well back from water's edge	Excellent for wildlife. Acorns eaten by mallard and pintail. High insect value – 423 associated invertebrates	20 m+
Birch	Downy birch does well on wet sites. The commoner silver birch requires drier sites	Seeds eaten by mallard and teal. Screening and sheltering. Silver birch has 334 associated invertebrate species	15 m+
Hawthorn	Hardy, quick-growing once established	Excellent for wildlife. Flowers and berries attract insects, birds and small mammals. Over 200 associated invertebrates. Seeds eaten by teal	0.5–5 m
Ash	Will grow in damp conditions and can tolerate seasonal water-logging	68 associated invertebrates	20 m+
Field maple	Attractive autumn colours	Over 50 associated invertebrates	5–15 m
Bramble	Very common in all habitats. Can be invasive	Fruits eaten by mallard, teal and pintail. Excellent nesting cover	0.5–5 m
Dog rose	Hardy, quick growing. Tolerates wet but not water-logging	Flowers and fruit attract insects and birds	0.5–5 m
Blackthorn	Can spread quickly without management	Over 150 associated invertebrates. Good, dense nesting cover for small birds	0.5–5 m
Hazel	Quick-growing, traditional coppice species	Over 100 associated invertebrates	5–15 m
Dogwood	Attractive red stems	Seeds attract birds	0.5–5 m
Holly	Useful provider of evergreen cover and shelter	100 associated invertebrates. Attracts birds	5–15 m

Table 6.1 continued

Species	General comments	Value to wildfowl and other wildlife
Bankside		
Meadowsweet	Found in damp areas	Dense clusters of creamy flowers attract insects
Great willowherb	Common in damp locations. May colonise naturally	Useful cover in nesting areas
Ragged robin	Typical wetland species with bright pink flowers	
Marginal and emergent plants		
Common reed	Useful for bank stabilisation, but can be very invasive and should only be planted in large or deep water bodies	Good cover. Excellent habitat for birds where dense stands occur
Great reedmace	Very invasive – should only be planted in large or deep water bodies. Tolerates some pollution and silting	Good cover. Some insect value and also value to amphibians, dragonflies and damselflies
Branched bur-reed	Common and widespread by rivers, canals and ponds. Can be invasive in shallow waters (0.5 m)	Seeds eaten by mallard. Good cover value
Bulrush	By rivers, lakes, ponds usually where there is much silt. (Should not be confused with the invasive great reedmace often called bulrush)	Seeds eaten by mallard and teal. Cover value
Common spike-rush	In marshes, wet meadows and by ditches, ponds, etc.	Seeds eaten by mallard, teal, shoveler. Cover value
Flowering rush	By ponds and ditches. Attractive pink flower heads	
Hard rush	Marshes and wet edges of ponds. Neutral to alkaline soils	Seeds eaten by wildfowl
Soft rush	Marshes and wet edges of ponds. Neutral to acid soils	Seeds eaten by wildfowl
Reed sweet-grass	Abundant by rivers, canals and ponds. Invasive in shallow areas	Seeds eaten by mallard. Leaves eaten by swan
Flote-grass	Common in slow-moving water. Tolerates fluctuating water levels. Can be invasive in small ponds	Seeds eaten by mallard. Leaves eaten by wigeon and swan
Reed canary-grass	Tolerates flooding and also dry conditions	Good cover for birds. Seeds eaten by mallard
Sedges	Large group of common water plants. Found in marshy areas and pond edges	Seeds eaten by mallard and other wildfowl. Can be good cover

(continued overleaf)

Table 6.1 continued

Species	General comments	Value to wildfowl and other wildlife
Great water dock	Wet places by and in ponds, lakes, streams and canals	Seeds eaten by mallard and teal
Marsh marigold	Large yellow flowers. Tolerates some dryness. Typical of marshes, wet grassland	Early flowering. Good for insects
Yellow flag	Quick-growing. Needs careful management in small ponds. Spreads rapidly. Attractive flowers	Provides cover for invertebrates
Water forget-me-not	Tolerates fluctuating water level and shade	
Bogbean	Attractive foliage and flowers. Can form dense mats	
Lesser spearwort	Wet places, common. Tolerates shade	Invertebrate habitat. Seeds eaten by birds
Greater spearwort	Marshes, fens and ditches	
Water mint	Common in ponds, ditches and wet places. Tolerates fluctuating water levels	

Submerged and floating-leaved plants

Species	General comments	Value to wildfowl and other wildlife
Mare's-tail	Locally common in ponds, lakes and slow streams. Can withstand moderately acid conditions. Tolerates fluctuating water levels	Seeds eaten by mallard, teal, shoveler. Good cover. Can attract insects for ducklings
Water-crowfoot	Various species of aquatic 'buttercups'. Common in fresh water	Seeds eaten by mallard, teal and shoveler, leaf and stem by wigeon, pochard, gadwall. Flowers attract insects. Good habitat for invertebrates and for newts
Broad-leaved pondweed	Common in water to depth of 1.5 m, normally 1 m. Tolerates acid waters. Often completely covers ponds. Not recommended for fisheries	Seeds eaten by mallard and teal. Good for invertebrates
Fennel-leaved pondweed	Frequent in fresh and brackish ponds, ditches, etc. Likes alkaline conditions. Will grow in polluted or turbid water	Seeds eaten by mallard, pintail, teal and pochard, tubers by mallard, leaf and stem by wigeon and gadwall. Good cover for invertebrates
Stonewort	These algae are fast-growing early colonisers. Abundant in fresh and brackish waters	Spores and whole plant eaten by pochard and teal
Starwort	Abundant on still and moving water. Very delicate plants with tiny yellow flowers	Eaten by wildfowl. Good cover for invertebrates

Table 6.1 continued

Species	General comments	Value to wildfowl and other wildlife
Yellow water-lily	Rooted in neutral or alkaline water up to 3 m deep. Can be invasive. Not recommended for fisheries. Tolerates some shade	Shelter for fish
White water-lily	Rooted in neutral or alkaline water up to 3 m deep. Can be invasive. Not recommended for fisheries	Shelter for fish
Fringed water-lily	Can be invasive, but attractive	Shelter for fish
Spiked water-milfoil	Rooted in water up to 2 m deep. With floating leaves and emergent flowers	Good habitat for invertebrates. Eaten by wildfowl
Arrowhead	Ponds, canals and ditches in shallow water (15 cm) and on margins	Tubers eaten by mallard and teal. Leaves also eaten
Amphibious bistort	Found on banks and down to 1 m. Tolerates extended drying and also flooding. Attractive flowers	Seeds eaten by mallard. Good cover for broods. Flower stalks attract insects, and provide food for ducklings

Free-floating plants

Species	General comments	Value to wildfowl and other wildlife
Duckweeds	Frequent in still water. May choke surface of ponds	Eaten by mallard, shoveler, teal and wigeon
Frogbit	Locally common on still water. Can form large mats requiring regular management	Invertebrate habitat, feeding area for ducklings and fish
Rigid horn-wort	Grows very rapidly and requires regular management	Good wildfowl food and invertebrate cover

illegal to remove any species that are protected under the Wildlife and Countryside Act 1981 (see the *Legislation and Regulations* booklet in the foundation module). Indeed, any pond containing a protected plant or animal is probably best not disturbed at all. The wetland and riparian plants on the protected list at present include triangular club-rush, water germander, rough marsh mallow, fen violet and ribbon-leaved water plantain. Even with common species, you should take plants only from sites where they are present in abundance. Rooted plants need to be dug out with a little care to avoid damaging the roots if they are to be successfully transplanted, and it is important to minimise disturbance to the rest of the pond. By transferring from an existing site, it is easier to be sure that the plants are appropriate for the particular site conditions. If plants are bought from a garden centre, check that they are suitable for your circumstances. Do not be tempted to buy rare species, at least at first, as they are less likely to succeed, and certainly avoid any exotic species, such as water fern and Australian swamp stonecrop, which are invading British fresh water. It is possible to grow some aquatic plants from seed, but using existing plants is much quicker and easier. One further possible source is the National Rivers Authority, which may be able to provide plant material from river dredging operations.

Trees and scrub are extremely valuable near a pond, but it is important that they are not too near. They must not be allowed to shade the water too much, as this will limit the potential of the aquatic plants, and the accumulating debris from overhanging branches will use up oxygen as it decays and require frequent clearance or the pond will slowly fill up.

One or two trees at the water's edge provide good cover for birds and animals and privacy and shelter for anglers and birdwatchers. The insects that live on the leaves and bark may fall into the water and be eaten by other invertebrates or fish. Fish also like to lie in the shade of overhanging vegetation. Otherwise, trees should be planted no nearer than one and a half times the height of a mature specimen of that species on the north and west sides of the pond, leaving the sunnier south and east sides open.

If wildfowl are to be encouraged to use the pond, some thought must be given to their natural flight lines and the prevailing wind direction. Ducks prefer a 30°–35° angle into the pond, which is not obscured by trees, for take-off and landing.

Trees should never be planted on retaining dams or embankments. Nor should they be planted on or near an impermeable lining sheet, as their roots may damage or puncture it.

Small, scrubby bushes with dense ground vegetation are important for many birds and amphibians, because of the cover that they provide. These can be planted between trees and extending closer to the pond.

An open area of grass with wild flowers adjacent to a pond, approximately 2–3 metres wide, provides a feeding and nesting area for wildfowl. If the site is not grassed already, a seed mixture selected for damp conditions can be used. 'Weeds', such as nettles and docks, will colonise naturally within a year and these may need controlling if they are not to dominate.

Plants at the water's edge are very important for the cover they provide for the pond's residents and visitors. This zone can be extensively planted, except around shallow bays where young birds will need clear access in and out of the water. Some of the plants of this zone, particularly common reed and great reedmace, can be extremely invasive and will rapidly spread at the expense of other species. They should only be planted in large water bodies, or they can be restricted by a deep water channel (at least 2 metres deep) around the clump.

Some plants with floating and/or submerged leaves can also be introduced, although it can be difficult to place these with precision. The main criterion for these plants is that the water depth is appropriate for the particular species. This information should be provided with shop-bought plants or, if they are transferred from another pond, note the depth from which they came.

Islands can also be planted, although their size will determine what is appropriate. Large islands can accommodate trees such as willows, but do bear in mind the need for access to manage them. If the island is intended as a nesting site for wildfowl, low scrub and ground vegetation are advisable, with a bare area for resting and preening.

Willows and poplars can be grown simply by taking a cutting from a parent tree and planting it in moist soil. It will rapidly take root.

At the water's edge, individual plants can be planted by pushing cuttings or whole, rooted plants into the mud and heeling them in. Many emergent and floating-leaved plants can be transplanted from nearby sites simply by taking a spadeful of mud complete with roots or rhizomes and putting it in the new pond. This can even be done by a mechanical digger. In deeper water, it may be necessary to weight the plants with stones to stop them floating up to the surface, or the roots can be tied into a hessian bag with soil and stones and then thrown in. Some plants are often supplied in weighted baskets or degradable pots or bags through which the roots can grow. These can simply be put in the pond at a point where the water is the right depth.

Any new plants, from young trees to grass seed mixtures, will need protection from farm animals and also from rabbits. This may mean that fencing is required at least until the plants are well established. Protection from ducks and fish may also be necessary.

When to plant

Planting of aquatic species is best carried out in April or May with the growing season ahead for the plants to establish themselves. Identifying plants to transfer from another pond may be difficult at this time of year, if the new growth is not showing after the winter dormancy period. Selecting the plants you want and marking them during the previous summer can make this easier.

Trees and other bankside plants will need to be watered in dry weather. Plants at the water's edge are obviously vulnerable to fluctuating water level, so some losses should be expected if a dry summer follows springtime planting. Planting can also be done in the autumn, but this is less successful, as the young plants have to endure the stresses of winter weather.

Animals

Invertebrates

A surprising number of invertebrates with the power of flight will colonise a new pond, as long as there is an existing water body nearby, say within 750 metres. Water-boatmen, beetles and dragonflies, among others, will investigate new waters quite quickly, and will stay if conditions suit them. Vegetation transplanted from another pond will almost certainly be carrying snails and their eggs, as well as those of many other invertebrates. Indeed, this is another good reason for using plants from an existing pond nearby. A bucketful of mud from the same source will also add to the invertebrate population.

Amphibians

Frogs, toads and newts may also arrive from other ponds in the neighbour-hood. Frogs and toads will travel up to about 1 kilometre from their home pond and newts about 500 metres, as long as there is good cover in permanent scrub and long grasses. Taking spawn and transferring it to a new pond reduces the uncertainty of colonisation, but should not be done before the aquatic vegetation has had a chance to become thoroughly established. Frog and toad spawn should preferably be taken from sites where it would otherwise perish. Frogs frequently lay spawn in ditches, even puddles that are bound to dry out before the tadpoles have matured. If you have to take spawn from another pond, find a site that has plenty, and only take a small amount. Taking spawn of the great crested newt is illegal.

Fish

Fish may also colonise naturally, but obviously only if there is a water connection to another pond or river. Fish should only be introduced where angling is one of the intended purposes of a pond, as the introduction of fish will cause a profound disturbance to the pond's ecosystem and unstocked ponds are becoming increasingly rare. To provide a valuable wildlife habitat, it is far better to allow a natural balance to evolve within the aquatic system.

If angling is the intended purpose of a new pond, it is important to wait at least one year before introducing fish. This allows the pond to stabilise and the new vegetation to become established. If the pond is planted in spring, stocking should not take place until the summer of the following year, approximately 18 months later.

Choosing fish species for introduction requires care and knowledge. Expert advice should be sought and is essential for game fish. In England, Fisheries Officers of the National Rivers Authority must be consulted, not only to provide this advice but also because there is a legal requirement to obtain their consent in the form of a stocking licence.

Birds
Many different birds will be attracted to a pond, as long as it can provide opportunities for finding food, shelter or nest-sites. These may well include wild duck, which will flight into the pond at dusk to feed. If shooting for sport is an intended use of the pond, the wild duck can be encouraged by supplementing the natural food with small, regular, daily feeds of wheat or barley. If the pond is not near a flight line, or is in a place where there is only a small local duck population, it may be necessary to release reared mallard, although this must be tightly controlled and managed. It is important not to overfeed the ducks and not to release too many, because excess feed combined with duck wastes can cause a deterioration in the water quality, and the vegetation is also likely to suffer from trampling and being eaten. Advice on release and all other aspects of management of a pond or lake for wild-fowl should be sought from The Game Conservancy (the address is in the *Helpful Organisations* booklet in the foundation module) (see also Appendix I).

Most birds and mammals can only be encouraged to visit a new pond by providing the right conditions of depth, shape and vegetation. If this is done, and assuming that good management maintains these inviting conditions, waiting and hoping is really all that remains to be done.

6.5   Creating wetlands

As mentioned at the beginning of this chapter, there are relatively few opportunities for creating new wetland areas, and those that there are tend to be small in scale. However, if plans for every new pond included an adjacent area of marsh, this would go some way towards redressing the balance in favour of this increasingly threatened habitat. Creating marshy areas next to ponds is fairly straightforward. It simply entails scraping or excavating an adjoining very shallow flat area that will be flooded when the pond is filled with water. If this work is done at the same time as the pond is dug, or when an excavator is on site for some other job, such as ditch clearance, the additional costs can be kept to a minimum.

Similar shallow areas can be excavated alongside watercourses, which will then flood naturally, and also in appropriate places adjacent to canals and existing ponds, lakes and reservoirs. As before, care must be taken to ensure that the site in question is not already a valuable habitat.

There may also be possibilities for creating small wetlands simply by accepting that some parts of some fields are permanently wet and allowing them to remain so. If boggy field corners are fenced from animals, this may provide the opportunity for a natural wetland flora to develop.

6.6 Deciding on options for managing your wet habitats

Having read in Chapters 5 and 6 about the range of options that can be adopted to improve existing wet habitats and create new ones, you should now decide which are most appropriate for the area that you are studying. Remember to base the decision on an integrated assessment (using the techniques described here and in the foundation book) and on a careful consideration of the land manager's objectives. Section 6.7 gives some examples from the two case studies.

6.7 Options for managing water and wetland habitats in the case study areas

Borders Farm

Much conservation work has already been undertaken, and brief details of this are provided for the three sites that we have considered.

Original use: Rushy area on farm.

Current use: Wildlife scrapes.

Aim: To create a series of interlinked scrapes of varying depth. Clay had already been removed from the site for lining the clay-lined pond near the farmhouse and facing-up the impoundment of Mossbrae Lochan. The site was reworked to give a wide range of habitat types and high edge-density in a small area.

Machinery used: Hymac-type excavator, two dumper trucks, hand labour.

Procedure: Wet ground reworked into a set of linked wetlands in a terraced fashion. Hand-cut turves introduced from wetlands nearby. Natural recovery of vegetation allowed. Fencing carried out to exclude stock.

Original use: Sitka plantation on wet marshy land.

Current use: Recreation, fishing and wildlife.

Aim: To dam a basin by construction of an impoundment and to create a large body of water by gathering a number of small burns and one large burn.

Machinery used: Hymac-type excavator, two dumper trucks (3 tonne), bulldozer (15 tonne), small bulldozer (10 tonne).

Procedure: Clear-fell of Sitka. Site levelled. Original vegetation left (to provide food for fish). Impoundment created (about 25 metres wide at base, approximately 1:4/1:3 batter). Draw-down pipe incorporated to keep water off site during work. Impoundment compacted with 15-tonne bulldozer, faced with clay, armoured with river-stone, filled from burn.

Construction details for past options

Site 1

Site 2

Silt-trap created with use of gabions. Spillway incorporated in outlet, reinforced with gabions and butyl liner. Note: Curvature of dam designed to avoid 'straight-line' appearance and create 'naturalness'.

Stocked with rainbow trout of accredited source.

Site 3

Original use: Boggy area; rough grazed.

Current use: Flight ponds.

Aim: To create two flight ponds for duck shooting. Shot approx six times in the season; fed every other day with barley (during the season).

Machinery used: Hymac-type excavator.

Procedure: Straightforward excavation. Spoil spread over adjacent ground. Varying depth. Many shallow areas and shallow pools adjacent. Wet character of adjacent land retained. Low impoundments. Overflow pipes used. Fenced against stock access.

Future options

In addition to the previous works, there are various points that are still being considered (see also Chapter 7).

▶ The large pond nearest the house suffered from an explosive growth of Canadian pondweed a couple of years ago. This had not been introduced intentionally and arrived either as a fragment on some other introduced plants, or on the feet of visiting birds (other water bodies in the area are known to have Canadian pondweed in them). The River Purification Board was consulted and an approved herbicide was used, with only limited success. Eventually the pond had to be hand weeded (having first shut off the water supply and pumped out some of the water).

▶ An option for improving Mossbrae Lochan would be the addition of a carefully designed floating island to provide a good resting and rooting habitat. However, the anchor lines for such a feature would interfere with fishing when the raft was removed during the season.

▶ A pond in the conifer plantation requires the reconstruction of a small sleeper dam, as the old one had been eroded away by backwash from the overspill.

▶ The wet areas on the hill land present plenty of opportunities for more ponds to be created. However, the cost of individual fencing against stock is considered prohibitive.

The River Ouse, Buckingham

As with all situations where a problem of flooding has been identified along a watercourse, there are four basic options for river and conservation management.

1 Do nothing.
2 Re-route the floodwater.
3 Provide balancing reservoir(s).
4 Increase the existing capacity of the river.

Option 1

In the case of the River Ouse at Buckingham, option 1 is not a realistic one, since urban development has already occurred and flooding cannot be tolerated in the urban area or downstream at anything greater than the present frequency.

Option 2 is also unacceptable, since creation of a totally new channel would be extremely expensive, even assuming a route could be found. However, this option has been employed at specific locations, by building high-level flood channels to bypass the three main meander loops above Maids Moreton weir.

Option 2

Option 3 presents a potentially attractive proposition, and was examined in some detail by the design engineers. In many studies, this option may provide the opportunity to create new wetland areas. However, to be effective, balancing reservoirs must, by their nature, be 'empty' at most times of the year, and so there are constraints on the nature and management of such areas. In the present case, it was proposed that flooding could be prevented if two dry interceptor reservoirs were constructed south of the river near Bourton Mill, into which storm water could discharge from the urban areas on that side of the valley. Discharges from the northern urban area would, however, still flow direct into the river, as there was no suitable location for a storage reservoir. In spite of this, it would be possible to solve the flooding problem if the two reservoirs south of the river were enlarged and a pumping station was built on the north side for use in extreme conditions.

Option 3

However, the preferred option was option 4: to improve the flood capacity of the existing river by a series of river improvements. Not only would the cost be two-thirds that of option 3, it could be carried out with minimal long-term environmental impact, and with many opportunities for enhancement of the wildlife resource, landscape and recreational potential of the river corridor.

Option 4

The process of scheme design and environmental impact appraisal in which conservation factors are integrated from the outset ensures that conservation 'costs' are taken on board as part of the accepted method of working.

Costs

The presence of dredging machinery on site meant that conservation enhancement options, such as the clearance of a silted-up, overgrown pond, could be done very quickly and cheaply as part of the overall programme. Similarly, methods of operation, such as dredging only two-thirds to three-quarters of the channel, were a matter of policy and good working practice rather than a cost.

Specific components of the programme, such as tree planting schemes, the use of natural stone pitching on Bourton weir and the creation of high-level flood channels across the meander loops, were identifiable conservation costs. However, even these were not costed as such, because they were treated as an integral part of meeting the engineering objectives in such a manner as also to meet the environmental objectives of the scheme. Rarely was it necessary to bring specific machinery to the site for conservation purposes that would not have already been on site at some stage of the scheme in any case.

The capacity of the channel was increased from 12 cubic metres per second (equivalent to a flood on average every two years) to 17 cubic metres per second at bankfull discharge. A variable amount of material was removed in order to achieve this, as marked on the design cross-sections (see Figure 6.3 overleaf). Generally, downstream at Maids Moreton weir the amount to be removed was less than upstream, and in places hardly any material at all was removed.

The channel improvements options

In the area upstream of the ring-road on the Bourton Mill site, the existing river system had fallen into disrepair, and because of the poor condition of the mill channel and mill weir, the majority of water flowed along the old bypass channel by means of a side weir, 80 metres upstream of the mill building, rather than through the mill as originally intended. To rectify this, a completely new 200 metre channel was cut bypassing the mill building. Flow was retained through the mill (by agreement with the owner) by means of a small intake structure and manually operated penstock valve off the new channel. One hundred and ten metres of the old bypass channel was infilled, from the side weir to its confluence with the backwater channel. However, the backwater channel that collects water from the north edge of the flood plain on the Bourton site was extended some 230 metres back by means of a new channel excavation, and connected to the main river at the upstream edge of the site. This created a new freshwater feed into the backwater channel, and also allowed the construction of three new amenity ponds along the backwater channel itself.

In addition to the above key features, two weirs were reconstructed, one at Bourton Mill on the new main river channel bypassing the old mill and the other at Maids Moreton, both built to the same level as they had been previously, in order to maintain the river regime upstream.

Protection of flora and fauna

Many of the environmental effects of the new works as described were of a positive nature, despite initial temporary disturbance during some of the works. Key features incorporated in the final detailed scheme design included:

▷ dredging from only one side of the channel;

▷ retaining marginal vegetation on the opposite bank and leaving undredged at least one-quarter to one-third of the channel width in all locations;

▷ retaining trees and bushes on the working bank;

▷ retaining undisturbed the three main meander loops, by creating new high-level artificial bypass channels to take the peak flood flows. Each channel is protected by an articulated, intermeshing concrete block mattress with an open structure. This has been topsoiled and seeded, and will be grazed by cattle;

▷ careful retention during dredging of existing gravel riffles and deep pools to protect key invertebrate and fish habitats;

▷ maintaining the existing river regime, in particular the deep slow-flowing sections immediately upstream of Maids Moreton weir used by tufted duck and little grebe, by rebuilding the weirs to existing heights;

▷ detailed on-site instruction of the dredgers to ensure that the exact river bank profiles were not trapezoidal and that wet ledges and shallow margins were incorporated whenever appropriate;

Enhancement and creation of new features

a major tree planting scheme in conjunction with local landowners and the BBDC. The majority of downstream sites are small (up to 100 trees) clumps of native hardwoods, including oak, ash, field maple, alder (as marked on Figure 6.3). In the Bourton Mill area, the BBDC has planted more extensively with advanced nursery stock and some standards, and used a wider variety of indigenous or damp-tolerant species in dense stands;

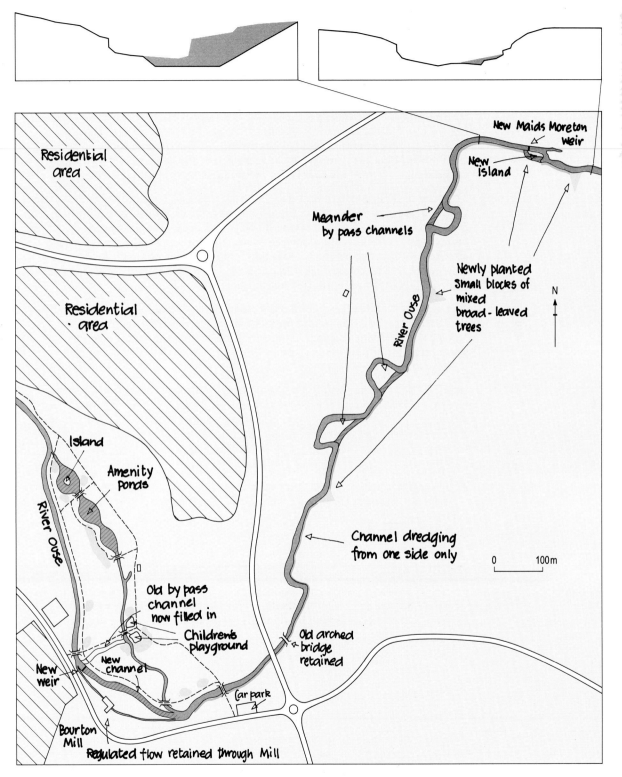

Figure 6.3   Map showing improvement works for River Ouse, Buckingham
(compare this with Figure 2.4 showing location before improvement works)

109

▷ creating three new ponds along the line of the new backwater channel on the Bourton Mill site, and clearing the two ponds at the downstream end of the scheme adjacent to the river;

▷ creating a new island at Maids Moreton weir, where a new subsidiary side weir has been incorporated into the design, isolating a small triangle of land, which has been planted up and retained as an island;

▷ creating a two-stage channel design for the new main river cut bypassing the old mill. This ensures that at low flow the river is still relatively narrow and deep, with a wide, wetted shelf (or berm) at water level, which is colonized by emergent species. At high flow, the berm becomes totally inundated, as part of a wider cross-section able to contain peak flood levels.

Cultural and landscape enhancement

The scheme will improve and develop landscape and amenity features in the river corridor, particularly on the upstream Bourton Mill site. The tree planting undertaken at this site will soften the views of urban areas on the valley sides, and help mask the electricity substation and the pump-house. The new footpaths and the backwater channel and ponds will be attractive features of this amenity parkland, while the removal of overhead electricity cables will further enhance the landscape.

The new weir on the new main river channel bypassing the old mill has been designed to fit into this landscape plan; its cascade structure and natural stone pitching form an attractive water feature near the main footpath. The alternative, a regular concrete structure, would have been cheaper, but unsympathetic to the site.

Finally, although not a protected structure, the fine old arched bridge downstream of the ring-road has been retained. This was achieved by constructing a concrete flume beneath it to speed flow through the arch and hence counter the constriction caused by its narrow width.

Chapter 7

IMPLEMENTING THE PLAN AND MONITORING PROGRESS

Using your assessment of the quality and potential of your land, you should have developed a clear idea of which management options are feasible in your situation. The options you choose to put into practice will depend on your objectives and the constraints affecting your use of the land.

If you are unclear or uncertain about what action to take at this or any other stage in the management planning process, it is a good idea to seek professional advice. This is most important when the contents of the management plan are being transferred to a detailed work plan, which describes when and where operations are to be done, who will do the work, the equipment needed, the expected costs and benefits, and how the results are to be monitored in the long term. (More information on the preparation of a formal plan of action can be found in Chapter 7 of the foundation book.)

Both a management plan and a work plan should be written before any work is done. Not only will this help to clarify the objectives for the planner, it will also provide agreed guidelines for the workforce, whether they are your own labour or contractors brought in to do the job. Equally important, grant aid is usually approved on the submission of an appropriate management/work plan, and normally approval should be obtained before any work is undertaken.

7.1 Grant aid

Grants for conservation work may be available to farmers and other individuals and groups from a number of different sources. Each grant-aiding organisation (see the *Helpful Organisations* booklet in the foundation module) has its own grant conditions. These are designed to ensure that the project is carried out correctly, and that the recipient will fulfil the objectives of the grant-awarding body. You should make sure that you understand the relevant conditions before applying for grant aid and, in particular, check whether prior approval is needed for any work. If work has started without approval being gained, grant aid may be forfeited. Although there may be several potential sources of grant aid for conservation work, it is generally the case that only one grant will be given for any individual project.

7.2 Costs

The main costs of any work to create or maintain water and wetlands will be from labour and equipment, especially if this has to be hired. In particular circumstances, additional costs will be incurred, for example the cost of stocking with fish for an angling enterprise. In addition, there are indirect costs for necessary items, such as training and the administration and management costs involved in grant and planning procedures.

Labour

Labour requirements for conservation work typically entail brief flurries of intense activity for major work like pond clearance or excavation, followed by several years with only occasional input. To clean out a pond 20–30 metres in diameter could take approximately 6–10 hours with a hydraulic or tractor excavator. This operation would need to be repeated approximately every 6–10 years for a lowland pond. In upland ponds, the vegetation is normally less prolific and there is less sedimentation, so the interval could be longer, say every 10–15 years. To excavate a new pond of similar size would take approximately two days, excluding time for levelling and landscaping. This would be for a simple excavation; constructing dams or other features would take longer.

If excavating machinery has to be brought on site from elsewhere specially for a job, better use can be made of it by taking the opportunity to employ it for one or two minor jobs as well. Hire is likely to be charged by the day, so it pays to keep an excavator busy for the entire hire period.

Keeping aquatic and bankside vegetation under control may need to be an annual event, depending on the types of plant and local conditions. Working on a small section of an area each year can keep this job to reasonable proportions. The real needs can only be judged from knowledge and experience of a site.

Where water is managed for a profit-making purpose as well as conservation, financial calculations will be centred on the viability of the business, and will include labour and training requirements. The labour input will vary greatly for the different options outlined in Chapter 4, from a fairly low input for producing reeds or willow products to a high input for waters managed for angling or shooting.

For conservation, it is important that all the people involved in the work at every level have some understanding of the aims of the project and how this is to be achieved. This is particularly important for excavator operators. They should be given clear and precise information on the size, shape and profile of the excavation. Wherever possible, verbal instruction should be reinforced by marker pegs and other indicators on the ground. Added to this should be an explanation of the general need to achieve a natural appearance, by avoiding straight lines and resisting the urge to 'tidy up' the landscape. Engaging people's interest in the purposes of a project as a means of improving a habitat for wildlife should help its chances of success.

Safety

Anyone working in or near water should be fully aware of the need for safety precautions. These will primarily be concerned with the potential danger from falling in and health hazards from polluted water. The former can usually be prevented with common sense, by avoiding deep mud, steep or slippery banks and by wearing appropriate footwear. If a job requires someone to get into the water, it is certainly inadvisable for that person to work alone.

Thorough hand-washing after any contact with surface water is advisable, because of the possibility of bacterial contamination. It is safer to assume that all waters, regardless of how clean they appear to be, are in fact contaminated, and to take the necessary precautions. In addition, it is sensible to obtain protection from tetanus by vaccination.

112

7.3   Legislation

Several different aspects of the practical conservation of water and wetlands are controlled by legislation. There are many Acts of parliament that are relevant, some referring to the whole of Great Britain and others to Scotland or England and Wales only. The separate countries also have separate statutory and regulatory organisations, which further complicates the picture. In addition, the laws and regulations change frequently. The *Legislation and Regulations* booklet in the foundation module contains further information on this subject. Box 7.1 (overleaf) summarises the possible consultative steps necessary when planning a new pond. If you are in any doubt as to whether legal permission or licence is required for any part of your plans, it is far better to consult the relevant authority in advance than to find out too late that this is the case.

7.4   Monitoring

The final stage of the management planning process does not bring the process to an end, but carries onwards and back to the assessment stages. The management plan and the work plan will need to be amended and updated in the light of developments, both expected and unforeseen, because however well planned and executed, the outcome of a particular project may not be exactly what was intended. There is always an element of uncertainty with any natural system – new plants may die back or, alternatively, may grow rapidly and dominate to the exclusion of others, a dry summer may jeopardise wetland areas, and so on. A particular management practice may have unforeseen 'knock-on' effects on other components of the system. For example, cutting back tree branches that are overhanging and shading a pond may cause one invasive species of water weed to take over the whole pond rather than encouraging the diverse plant population that was hoped for.

Monitoring is a procedure that can take place at several different levels. At its simplest, it can take the form of casual observation whenever you walk close to the pond, stream, marsh or other water or wetland area. You may notice that duckweed has spread rather too far, or that a willow branch has cracked and may shortly fall into the water, or that newly planted shrubs have been nibbled by rabbits. Frequent observation at this level should also be a source of pleasure to you, as this will be your opportunity to enjoy the fruits of your labours and perhaps see some of the wildlife for which the plan was made. At this level of monitoring, you will probably notice significant problems that need to be dealt with, but it is unlikely to reveal satisfactorily the full development of the site as a wildlife habitat and landscape feature. For this, a slightly more formalised monitoring programme is required. You should devise a schedule for regular observation of specific features of interest. It is most important that these observations are recorded for future reference, so that gradual changes, both improvements and deterioration, can be identified. A simple method of recording is to take a photograph from the same spot on each monitoring visit. The position chosen could be one of the viewpoints used for landscape assessment in Chapter 2. In addition, a few short notes in the form of a checklist would be useful. This could include such things as water level, visible signs of pollution, percentage cover of floating-leaved plants, growth of trees and bushes

Box 7.1 Ponds and the law: checklist

Does the site have any protected status,
e.g. Site of Special Scientific Interest?

☐ NO   ☐ YES ——————————————————————→ Consult the NCC. It will be able to provide advice on
                                                                                              wildlife interest and how to manage it.

Is the pond to be supplied by water from abstraction, ←——————————————————— OK ☐
impoundment or diversion of a watercourse?

☐ NO   ☐ YES ——————————————————————→ Consult the regional NRA to obtain a licence.

Is the pond for an operation that is potentially polluting, ←——————————— OK ☐
e.g. a vegetable washing plant, fish farming etc.?

☐ NO   ☐ YES ——————————————————————→ Consult the regional NRA/RPB.

Is the pond for non-agricultural purposes, ←——————————————————— OK ☐
e.g. landscape, amenity, wildlife, sporting etc.?

☐ NO   ☐ YES ——————————————————————→ Consult the County, Regional or District Council regarding
                                                                                              planning permission.

Does the supplying watercourse have any migratory salmon/trout? ←————— OK ☐
This may need to checked by professional electro-shocking.

☐ NO   ☐ YES ——————————————————————→ Consult the regional NRA, the district SFB, the River
                                                                                              Commissioners or the SOAFD.

Does the proposed pond exceed five and a half million gallons in ←——— OK ☐
volume (25 000 cubic metres)? This is equivalent to 1 hectare at
an average depth of 2.5 metres.

☐ NO   ☐ YES ——————————————————————→ The pond falls under the Reservoirs Act 1975. It must be
                                                                                              constructed under the supervision of a qualified civil engineer
                                                                                              and be checked regularly.

Have you informed downstream riparian owners and others who ←——————— OK ☐
may be affected about your plans? They have a right to the
continuation of the water supply to which they are accustomed.

☐ YES   ☐ NO ——————————————————————→ Do so!

Have you informed the NRA/RPB of your plans? Asking their ←—————————— OK ☐
advice and keeping them informed from an early stage will prevent
any unexpected problems, and may save money.

☐ YES   ☐ NO ——————————————————————→ Do so!

Are there plans to introduce salmon or non-native fish? ←————————————— OK ☐

☐ NO   ☐ YES ——————————————————————→ Obtain permission from the NRA/district SFB and consult
                                                                                              the MAFF/SOAFD.

Will any fish be introduced? ←—————————————————————————— OK ☐

☐ NO   ☐ YES ——————————————————————→ Obtain a licence from the NRA. Ponds should be screened
                                                                                              to prevent movement into or out of them.

Are there any plans to introduce wildfowl? ←—————————————————— OK ☐

☐ NO   ☐ YES ——————————————————————→ Seek advice from The Game Conservancy. It is illegal to
                                                                                              release non-native waterfowl into the wild unless they are
                                                                                              pinnioned or clipped (i.e. flightless).   OK ☐

Do you intend to introduce plants from another pond in the area? ←—————

☐ NO   ☐ YES ——————————————————————→ The Wildlife and Countryside Act 1981 states that no plant
                                                                                              may be dug up without the permission of the owner of the
                                                                                              land on which it is growing. In addition, certain rare plants
                                                                                              are completely protected and may not be removed at all.
DIG THE POND ←———————————————————————— OK ☐ NCC or F(F)WAG local officers can advise on this.

F(F)WAG: Farming (Forestry) and Wildlife Advisory Group   RPB: River Purification Board
MAFF: Ministry of Agriculture, Fisheries and Food   SFB: Salmon Fisheries Board
NCC: Nature Conservancy Council   SOAFD: Scottish Office, Agriculture and Fisheries Department
NRA: National Rivers Authority

(Source: Adapted from Countryside Commission for Scotland/Nature Conservancy Council, 1990)

or anything else that you feel is important. You must devise a schedule for monitoring to suit your own timetable, but taking a photograph and making a few notes will not take long, and should, if possible, be repeated every three months or so. This will provide information on seasonal variations, as well as accumulating a valuable archive of long-term developments. In addition, it may bring potential difficulties to your notice before they become real problems and, it is hoped, make them simpler and cheaper to rectify. These data should not simply be stored away to gather dust; they should be used to amend and update the management and work plans in response to the changes revealed.

By regularly monitoring the site, looking at its development as a habitat and a landscape feature, as well as watching out for any signs of damage or failure, then the water or wetland can be managed to maintain the optimum conditions for wildlife. Things may not turn out in quite the way you had planned but, with a flexible approach to management planning, conservation should be well served.

7.5 Monitoring of water and wetland habitats in the case study areas

Borders Farm

The keeper on the farm, who had an active interest in the design and construction of the pond and wetland features, is equipped with a checklist to use periodically to ensure that all inlets, outlets, impoundments, stock fences and facilities (e.g. fishing hut, boat, etc.) are in a good condition and are functioning correctly. It is felt by the landowner that a failure to monitor and manage all aspects of the holding will result in a loss of the desired overall effect.

In the long term, each feature will receive attention as need is perceived. There is no formal monitoring of plant or animal species composition, as in general there are too many other jobs to be done on the farm. If anything goes wrong, however, for example a pollution problem occurs, this would soon be noticed and corrected accordingly.

Nevertheless, there are certain future management needs that can be foreseen for the three selected sites.

▶ Loss of open water to progressively more dominant wetland plants will result in a reduced species diversity. It is intended that, as this succession occurs, ponds will be excavated on a rotation, ensuring that there is always a valuable refuge area at any one time. *Site 1*

▶ Willows and alders will be periodically coppiced to ensure that their growth is not out of scale with the wetland features. Repeated coppicing should give low, dense growth, providing good shelter and cover for birds and invertebrates.

▶ Inlets and outlets will be frequently checked and any problems, such as blockages, will be addressed. *Site 2*

▶ Opportunities for opening up and diversifying the south-west/southern shore are being considered.

▶ As with Site 1, there will be a need for periodic coppicing of newly planted trees to give low, tight cover. The southernmost of the two ponds has bypassed its overflow/outlet and the route currently taken by the water is eroding rapidly. This will be addressed in the near future.

▶ There has been some recent deposition of sediment at the entrance to the southernmost pond. While this provides another, different habitat, it could spread into the rest of the pond. An excavator will periodically clear this material. The site has a gated entrance to allow for this sort of management requirement.

The River Ouse, Buckingham

Regular monitoring has occurred, both of the wildlife resource and of the progress of the engineering works as they have been carried out.

The river corridor survey of the whole stretch undertaken in Summer 1987 was repeated again during Summer 1990 by the same field surveyor. This later survey showed that much of the vegetation had been successfully retained along the channel as had been intended in the plans for the scheme. Further surveys will be necessary to monitor the impact of the scheme in the downstream sections which had not been completed by Summer 1990.

Low river levels in Summer 1990 meant that there was little flow in the Bourton Mill site and abundant algae had developed, no doubt in response to enrichment caused by excavation of the new bypass channel around the mill. The new watercourse has colonised very quickly, with the wet shelf of the two-stage channel having abundant growth in its first season of plants such as water forget-me-not, bur-reed and water-cress, with arrowhead and water-crowfoot also present in the channel. However, loss of marginal plants was evident where the river edge had been too closely dredged just upstream of the ring-road.

Monitoring of the operation itself was undertaken by a local archaeologist as agreed, and also by the BBDC and conservation staff of Anglian Water Authority as work progressed. In addition, a resident engineer and site foreman oversaw the physical and structural work in great detail. Their daily presence helped to ensure that the contract was closely followed and that no accidental damage was done to important areas.

FURTHER READING

Agricultural Development and Advisory Service/ Mathieson, J (1986) Leaflet P3026 *Farm Ponds: Design and Construction*, MAFF/HMSO, London

Agricultural Development and Advisory Service/ Pugh, G (1986) Leaflet P3025 *Farm Ponds: Management and Maintenance*, MAFF/HMSO, London

Arnold, E N, Burton, J A, Overden, D W (1978) *The Reptiles and Amphibians of Britain and Europe*, Collins, London

Baines, C (1984) *How to Make a Wildlife Garden*, Elm Tree Books, London

British Association for Shooting and Conservation (undated) *Ponds and Lakes for Shooting and Conservation*, BASC, Wrexham, Clwyd

British Trust for Conservation Volunteers/Brooks, A (1981) *Waterways and Wetlands: A Practical Handbook*, BTCV, Wallingford, Oxfordshire

Broads Authority (1987) *Broads Plan*, Broads Authority, Norwich

Chaplin, P H (1989) *Waterway Conservation*, Whittet Books, London

Chinery, M (1976) *The Insects of Britain and Northern Europe*, Collins, London

Clegg, J (1974) *Freshwater Life*, Frederick Warne, London

Clegg, J (1980) *The Observer's Book of Pond Life*, Frederick Warne, London

Conservation in Agricultural Education Guidance Group/Farming and Wildlife Advisory Group CAE Leaflet No. 10 *Farm Ditches*, CAEGG/FWAG, Sandy, Bedfordshire

Conservation in Agricultural Education Guidance Group/Farming and Wildlife Advisory Group CAE Leaflet No. 12 *Upland Drainage – Open Ditch Drainage of Hill Peats*, CAEGG/FWAG, Sandy, Bedfordshire

Conservation in Agricultural Education Guidance Group/Farming and Wildlife Advisory Group CAE Leaflet No. 24 *Irrigation*, CAEGG/FWAG, Sandy, Bedfordshire

Croft, P S (1986) *A Key to the Major Groups of British Freshwater Invertebrates*, Field Studies Council, Shrewsbury

Countryside Commission (1987) *Landscape Assessment. A Countryside Commission Approach*, CCD 18, CC, Cheltenham, Gloucestershire

Countryside Commission for Scotland/Nature Conservancy Council (1990) Information Sheet *Creating Ponds and Conserving Wetlands*, CCS, Perth

Doherty, J and Pilkington, J (1983) *Hampshire's Countryside Heritage – Rivers and Wetlands*, Hampshire County Council

Fitter, R, Fitter, A, Blamey, M (1978) *The Wild Flowers of Britain and Northern Europe*, Collins, London

Forestry Commission (undated) *Forests and Water: Guidelines*, Forestry Commission, Edinburgh

Hammond, C O (1985) *The Dragonflies of Great Britain and Ireland*, Harley Books, Colchester, Essex

Haslam, S M, Sinker, C A, Wolseley, P A (1975) *British Water Plants*, Field Studies Council, Shrewsbury

Hayman, P (1979) *Birds*, Mitchell Beazley, London

Institute of Water and Environmental Management (1989) *Agriculture and the Environment*, Technical Papers and Proceedings of Annual Symposium 1989, IWEM, London

Jeffries, M and Mills, D (1990) *Freshwater Ecology*, Belhaven Press, London

Lewis, G and Williams, G (1984) *Rivers and Wildlife Handbook*, Royal Society for the Protection of Birds and Royal Society for Nature Conservation, Sandy, Bedfordshire

Ministry of Agriculture, Fisheries and Food (1980) *Guidelines for the Use of Herbicides in or near Watercourses and Lakes B2078*, MAFF Publications, London

Mitchell, A (1978) *The Trees of Britain and Northern Europe*, Collins, London

Moore, P D (1980) *Wild Flowers*, Mitchell Beazley, London

Morris, P (ed) (1980) *Natural History of the British Isles*, Country Life Books, Richmond, Surrey

Nature Conservancy Council/Countryside Commission (1980) Countryside Conservation Handbook *Leaflet 5: Farm Ponds*, CC (with Forestry Commission, MAFF and NCC), Cheltenham, Gloucestershire

Nature Conservancy Council/Newbold, C, Honnor, J, Buckley, K (1989) *Nature Conservation and the Management of Drainage Channels*, NCC, Peterborough, Hampshire

Nature Conservancy Council/Newbold, C, Purseglove, J, Holmes, N (1983) *Nature Conservation and River Engineering*, NCC, Peterborough, Hampshire

Newbold, C (1977) Wetlands and agriculture. In: *Conservation and Agriculture*, Davidson, J and Lloyd, R (eds), John Wiley, Chichester, Sussex

Newbold, C (1988) Wetland management, agricultural management and nature conservation. In: *Environmental Management in Agriculture*, Park, J R (ed), Belhaven Press, London

Peterson, R, Mountfort, G, Hallam, P A D (1974) *The Birds of Britain and Europe*, Collins, London

Probert, C (1989) *Pearls in the Landscape – The Conservation and Management of Ponds*, Farming Press, Ipswich, Suffolk

Purseglove, J (1988) *Taming the Flood*, Oxford University Press

Ritchie, J and MacMullen, R/Norfolk Farming and Wildlife Advisory Group (1987) *Farm Pond Management – A Practical Guide for Farmers and Advisers*, Norfolk FWAG/The Environmental Research Fund, Norwich

Rushford, K (1980) *Trees*, Mitchell Beazley, London

Solbe, J F de L G (ed) (1986) *Effects of Land Use on Fresh Waters – Agriculture, Forestry, Mineral Exploitation, Urbanisation*, Ellis Horwood, Chichester, Sussex

Street, M (1989) *Ponds and Lakes for Wildfowl*, The Game Conservancy, Fordingbridge, Hampshire

Water Authorities Association/Ministry of Agriculture, Fisheries and Food (1988) *Water Pollution from Farm Waste*, WAA, London

Wilson, R and Lee, P (1982) *The Marshland World*, Blandford Press, Blandford, Dorset

GLOSSARY

Alluvial Material deposited by streams and rivers.

Bankfull capacity Volume of water contained in a river channel when the water level is at, but not over, the top of the bank.

Batter Slope of a bank, expressed either as a ratio of horizontal distance to vertical distance (e.g. 1:2) or as the angle of slope in degrees (e.g. 63°).

Bay Recess in the water margin of a pond or lake.

Berm Shelf or ledge in the bank of a watercourse or water body.

Blanket bog Extensive area of acid *mire* found on flat and gently sloping ground where rainfall is high.

Carnivore Animal that eats the flesh of other animals.

Catchment area Area of land that collects and feeds water to a watercourse or wetland.

Crustacean Member of a group of *invertebrate* animals with an external skeleton, which includes shrimps, crabs, woodlice, etc.

Dissolved oxygen Oxygen dissolved in water.

Drain Ditch alongside a field designed to collect and remove drainage water.

Draw-down Localised lowering of the *water table* around a *groundwater* abstraction point.

Dyke Ditch or watercourse that functions, at least in part, as a barrier; in Scotland, a drystone wall.

Eutrophic Water of high productivity, rich in organic and mineral nutrients.

Faggoting Method of bank protection using bundles of long twigs (faggots) placed along the water's edge and pegged down.

Flash Small depression with shallow water, which may be natural or excavated.

Flood meadow Pasture adjacent to a river that is regularly inundated by natural flooding.

Flood plain Flat land on either side of a river over which flood waters spread, although this may be prevented by flood protection works.

Flume Artificial channel built to maximise flow-through efficiency.

Flush Area of permanently wet ground around a spring.

Fluvio-glacial Material transported and deposited by rivers and glaciers during the Ice Ages.

Gabion baskets Baskets, usually made of galvanised wire (traditionally of wicker), filled with stones, crushed concrete or earth and used for bank reinforcement.

Groundwater Water stored in the pores and voids of rocks in the saturated zone below the *water table*.

Hardness Property of water reflecting the quantity of dissolved calcium (and magnesium) salts; in domestic usage, more soap is needed to make a lather with hard water than with soft.

Headwater Part of a river system near to the source.

Herbivore Animal that eats plants.

Hill gripping Land drainage technique in upland areas involving cutting closely spaced, steep-sided, open *drains*.

Hydrological system Water system, i.e. surface waters, *groundwater*, soil moisture and atmospheric moisture and the interactions between them.

Impoundment Reservoir.

Inby land On a hill farm, term used to describe land close to the farmhouse, generally improved pasture.

Invertebrate Animal without a backbone.

Mesotrophic Water of medium productivity.

119

Mire Area of permanently wet peat; includes bog (acid) and fen (alkaline).

Mole drain Unlined sub-surface enclosed channel made by a special tractor-pulled plough.

Niche Role of a plant or animal within its community, which determines its activities and relationships with other organisms and its environment.

Non-point sources Diffuse sources of water pollution that do not emanate from a single location.

Ochre Natural pigment caused by the bacterial oxidation of iron in previously water-logged soil following exposure to air frequently as a result of land drainage. The colour may be brown, yellow or red.

Oligotrophic Water of low productivity, low in plant nutrients.

Osier Willow (*Salix viminalis* and *S. purpurea*) traditionally grown to produce slender rods for basket-making.

Peatland Area with peaty soil, that is soil made up entirely of organic remains.

pH Quantitative expression denoting the acidity or alkalinity of a solution or soil. It has a scale of 0 to 14; pH 7 is neutral, below 7 is acid and above 7 is alkaline.

Photosynthesis Synthesis, in green plants, of organic compounds from carbon dioxide and water using light energy from the sun.

Piped drain Underdrain lined with a pipe designed to collect and carry percolating water. Pipe materials include tiles (porous, clay pipe), perforated plastic pipe and also concrete, steel, etc.

Poaching Trampling by livestock causing land to break up into wet muddy patches.

Pollarded Tree that has been cut 2–4 metres above ground level and then allowed to regrow.

Pool Area of deeper water within a watercourse; pond, especially within a wetland.

Potable water Water that is fit to drink.

Puddled clay Traditional pond and waterway lining material, made by pounding clay and water to make a dense mass resistant to water penetration.

Respiration Process in which plants and animals derive energy by means of internal chemical reactions, generally using oxygen and giving out carbon dioxide.

Revetment Facing built to support a bank.

Rhyne Somerset name for a permanently wet ditch.

Riffle Shallow area in a watercourse, usually in fairly fast-flowing water and with a stone or gravel substrate.

Ruderal Plant living in wasteland near habitation.

Shoal Shallow area in a watercourse caused by deposition of sediment.

Spit Small promontory extending into a body of water.

Splash See *Flash*.

Substrate Literally underlayer; the material on the bottom of a river, pond, etc.

Succession Replacement of one type of community by another, shown by progressive changes in vegetation and animal life.

Suspended solids Particulate material held in suspension by moving water; a standard test in water analysis to determine the weight of solids suspended in a known volume of water.

Trafficability Ease of access for field activities by vehicles or animals.

Turbidity Reduced transparency caused, in water, by *suspended solids*.

Washland Area of frequently flooded flat land adjacent to a river.

Water meadow Waterside meadow with a managed regime of flooding.

Water table Level below which the soil/rock is permanently saturated.

Withy bed Term used in some regions to describe a bed of *osier* willow.

Appendix III

SCIENTIFIC NAMES FOR PLANT SPECIES

Alder *Alnus glutinosa*

Arrowhead *Sagittaria sagittifolia*

Ash *Fraxinus excelsior*

Asphodel, Bog *Narthecium ossifragum*

Avens, Water *Geum rivale*

Birch *Betula* spp

    Downy *B. pubescens*

    Silver *B. pendula*

Bistort, Amphibious *Polygonum amphibium*

Blackthorn *Prunus spinosa*

Bladderwort *Utricularia* spp

Bogbean *Menyanthes trifoliata*

Bog moss *Sphagnum* spp

Bramble *Rubus fruticosus*

Brooklime *Veronica beccabunga*

Bulrush (see Club-rush, Reedmace)

Bur-reed *Sparganium* spp

    Branched *S. erectum*

Chickweed, Water *Myosoton aquaticum*

Cinquefoil, Marsh *Potentilla palustris*

Club-rush *Scirpus* spp

    Common (Bulrush) *S. lacustris*

    Triangular *S. triqueter*

Comfrey *Symphytum officinale*

Cotton-grass *Eriophorum* spp

Crowfoot (see Water-crowfoot)

Cuckoo flower (Lady's smock) *Cardamine pratensis*

Dock, Water *Rumex hydrolapathum*

Dogwood *Cornus sanguinea*

Duckweed *Lemna* spp

Elder *Sambucus nigra*

Fern, Water *Azolla filiculoides*

Figwort, Water *Scrophularia auriculata*

Flag, Yellow (Yellow iris) *Iris pseudacorus*

Flote-grass *Glyceria fluitans*

Forget-me-not, Water *Myosotis scorpioides*

Frogbit *Hydrocharis morsus-ranae*

Galingale, Brown *Cyperus fuscus*

Germander, Water *Teucrium scordium*

Gypsywort *Lycopus europaeus*

Hawthorn *Crataegus monogyna*

Hazel *Corylus avellana*

Heath, Cross-leaved *Erica tetralix*

Holly *Ilex aquifolium*

Hornwort *Ceratophyllum* spp

    Rigid *C. demersum*

Iris (see Flag)

Loosestrife, Purple *Lythrum salicaria*

Mallow, Rough marsh *Althaea hirsuta*

Maple, Field *Acer campestre*

Mare's-tail *Hippuris vulgaris*

Marigold, Marsh *Caltha palustris*

Meadowsweet *Filipendula ulmaria*

Mint, Water *Mentha aquatica*

Moor-grass, Purple *Molinia caerulea*

Oak *Quercus robur*

Osier (see Willow)

Pondweed *Potamogeton* spp

    Bog *P. polygonifolius*

    Broad-leaved *P. natans*

    Fennel-leaved *P. pectinatus*

    Shining *P. lucens*

Pondweed, Canadian *Elodea canadensis*

Pondweed, Horned *Zanichellia palustris*

Ragged robin *Lychnis flos-cuculi*

Reed, Common *Phragmites australis*

Reed canary-grass *Phalaris arundinacea*

Reed sweet-grass *Glyceria maxima*

Reedmace *Typha* spp

    Great (Bulrush) *T. latifolia*

    Lesser (Lesser bulrush) *T. angustifolia*

Rose, Dog *Rosa canina*

Rush *Juncus* spp

    Hard *J. inflexus*

    Soft *J. effusus*

    Sharp-flowered *J. acutiflorus*

Rush, Flowering *Butomus umbellatus*

Sedge *Carex* spp

    Greater pond *C. riparia*

    Greater tussock *C. paniculata*

Soldier, Water *Stratiotes aloides*

Small-reed, Purple *Calamagrostis canescens*

Spearwort *Ranunculus* spp

    Adder's tongue *R. ophioglossifolius*

    Greater *R. lingua*

    Lesser *R. flammula*

Speedwell, Water *Veronica catenata*

Spike-rush, Common *Eleocharis palustris*

Starwort *Callitriche* spp

Stonecrop, Australian swamp *Crassula helmsii*

Stonewort *Chara* spp and *Nitella* spp

Sundew *Drosera* spp

Sycamore *Acer pseudoplatanus*

Violet, Fen *Viola persicifolia*

Water-cress *Nasturtium officinale*

Water-crowfoot *Ranunculus* spp

    Celery-leaved crowfoot *R. sceleratus*

    River water-crowfoot *R. fluitans*

    Stream water-crowfoot *R. penicillatus*

Water-dropwort, River *Oenanthe fluviatalis*

Water-lily, Fringed *Nymphoides peltata*

Water-lily, White *Nymphaea alba*

Water-lily, Yellow *Nuphar lutea*

Water-milfoil *Myriophyllum* spp

    Spiked *M. spicatum*

Water-plantain *Alisma plantago-aquatica*

Water-plantain, Ribbon-leaved *Alisma gramineum*

Waterwort *Elatine* spp

Willow *Salix* spp

    Crack *S. fragilis*

    Cricket-bat *S. alba* var. *coerulea*

    Goat *S. caprea*

    Grey (Common sallow) *S. cinerea*

    Osier *S. viminalis, S. purpurea*

Willowherb, Great *Epilobium hirsutum*

Woundwort, Marsh *Stachys palustris*

Acknowledgements

The Open University course team is greatly indebted to the many people, with a wide range of experience of countryside management, who have contributed to the development of this teaching programme.

First, we must acknowledge the very generous financial support of the Nature Conservancy Council, along with the Esmée Fairbairn Charitable Trust and the Ernest Cook Trust.

We also value the comments and the support of the external assessor, Professor Bryn Green, The Sir Cyril Kleinwort Professor of Countryside Management, Wye College, University of London.

Thirdly, we are extremely grateful to the two consultants who provided the case study material: J Roberts (Conservation Adviser, Lothians Farming, Forestry and Wildlife Advisory Group) and C Spray (Recreation and Conservation Manager, Northumbrian Water plc, formerly Conservation Officer, National Rivers Authority, Anglia Region).

Finally, we would like to thank the many other people who provided source material for the book or read and commented on preliminary drafts:

J Biggs (Pond Action)

J Grice (British Waterways Board)

A Heaton (National Rivers Authority)

S Hodgson
(British Trust for Conservation Volunteers)

R Howell (National Rivers Authority)

G Kerby (Agricultural Training Board)

D Moore (Anglian Water plc)

C Newbold (Nature Conservancy Council)

I Ridge (Open University)

T Rowell (Environmental Consultant)

R Simpson (Countryside Commission)

M Street (A R C Wildfowl Centre)

D Ward (Royal Society for the Protection of Birds)

D Waters (Bristol University)

Grateful acknowledgement is made to the following sources for permission to use material in this book:

Text

Box 7.1: Adapted from CCS *Information Sheet Plants 9.1.1*, copyright © 1990 Countryside Commission for Scotland, research by Nature Conservancy Council.

Figures

Figures 3.3, 3.4 and 3.5: Redrawn from Clegg, J (1974) *Freshwater Life*, Frederick Warne and Co. Ltd, copyright © John Clegg; *Figures 5.1, 5.2, 5.3 and 5.4*: Redrawn from Lewis, G and Williams, G (1984) *Rivers and Wildlife Handbook*, Royal Society for the Protection of Birds and Royal Society for Nature Conservation; *Figures 6.1 and 6.2*: From BASC *Ponds and Lakes for Shooting and Conservation*, copyright © The British Association for Shooting and Conservation.

Tables

Table 5.1: Adapted from Brooks, A (1981) *Waterways and Wetlands: A Practical Handbook*, copyright © 1981 British Trust for Conservation Volunteers; *Tables 5.2 and 5.3*: Redrawn from Lewis, G and Williams, G (1984) *Rivers and Wildlife Handbook*, Royal Society for the Protection of Birds and Royal Society for Nature Conservation.

Index

vegetation, wetland: management and maintenance 31, 78; *see also* carr, reedbeds *and* wet grasslands

W

wading birds: habitat requirements 40, 55, 93, 94 (case study areas) 49, 59, 64; *see also* birds

walkers, walking 54, 58: case study areas 23, 64–5

washlands 35

wastes and wastewater 32, 54, 62, 69: agricultural 5, 17, 33, 35, 41, 54, 55, 57–8, 62, 76–7; fish farming 60; industrial 5, 33, 41, 57, 62; oil 17, 77–8; storage 58, 77; toxic 33, 57; *see also* toxic substances; transport 58, 62, 77–8; urban and domestic 5, 57; *see also* rubbish and litter *and* sewage

water abstraction 9, 34–5, 54–5, 61, 65, 69, 70, 89, 93: licences 6, 61

Water Act 1989 61

water birds, *see* waterfowl/

wildfowl

water chemistry 31–2, 73

water meadows 35

water quality: case study area 51–2, 66, 68; criterion, habitat value 46; indicators 41–2; management 56–8, 76–8; *see also* pollution *and* wastes and wastewater

water quantity and levels 34–5, 55, 56: fluctuations 34–5, 42; management 57, 70–6, 89–90; *see also* flood control

water shrews: habitat requirements 40, 44, 84, 85; *see also* mammals, aquatic

water table 5, 34–5, 55, 56, 89, 90

water voles: habitat requirements 40–1, 44, 84, 85; *see also* mammals, aquatic

waterfowl/wildfowl: case study area 49, 64; see also flight ponds; habitat requirements 6, 9, 30, 40, 42, 60, 69, 71, 92–4, 102, 104;

hazards 60; new ponds 91–3, 104; *see also* birds and wading birds

watersports 54, 58, 62, 86, 87

weirs 73: case study area 110

wet ditches: animals and plants 16, 31, 34, 40, 56, 88; defined 8; deposition and sedimentation 75; management and maintenance 5, 16, 56, 70, 75, 77, 79, 80, 104; origins 9, 16, 62; pollution 62, 77; uses 8, 56; *see also* land drainage

wet grasslands: management 71, 76, 78; *see also* vegetation, wetland

wet woodlands, *see* carr

Wildlife and Countryside Act 1981 40, 44, 101

willows 79, 102–3: case study area 49, 51; crops 61; management and maintenance 61, 102–3

withy beds 61

work plan 111, 113, 114